CACHE
Foundation
Award

Caring for Children

2nd edition

www.heinemann.co.uk

✓ Free online support
✓ Useful weblinks
✓ 24 hour online ordering

01865 888118

Penny Tassoni

Heinemann

Part of Pearson

Heinemann is an imprint of Pearson Education Limited, a company incorporated in England and Wales, having its registered office at Edinburgh Gate, Harlow, Essex, CM20 2JE. Registered company number: 872828

www.heinemann.co.uk

Heinemann is a registered trademark of Pearson Education Limited

Text © Penny Tassoni, 2009

First published 2009

13 12 11 10 09
10 9 8 7 6 5 4 3 2 1

British Library Cataloguing in Publication Data
A catalogue record for this book is available from the British Library.

ISBN 978 0 435987 04 6

Edited by Lucy Hyde
Designed by Woodenark Studio
Typeset by Phoenix Photosetting, Chatham, Kent
Illustrated by Jo Goodberry/Tek Art
Cover design by Pearson Education LTD 2009
Picture research by Susie Prescott
Cover photo/illustration © Bon Appetit/Alamy
Printed in Italy

Author acknowledgements
I would like to thank the Heinemann team for putting this edition together, particularly Virginia Carter who has been a wonderful support for this and other projects. I would also like to thank Lucy Hyde for her help in producing this new edition. Finally, I must thank Jean-Michel and my daughters for their continued support in my work.

Photo acknowledgements
The author and publisher would like to thank the following individuals and organisations for permission to reproduce photographs: Bananastock/Imagestate pp8, 25, 53, 70, 83, 85, 107, 137, 148, 152, 171, 187; Blend Images/Alamy p31; BLOOMimage/Getty Images p64; Brian Summers/First Light/Getty Images p162; Bubbles Photolibrary/Alamy p12; Catherine Servel/Taxi/Getty Images p47; David Noton Photography/Alamy p172; Fancy/Photolibrary.com p4; Gaetano Images Inc./Alamy p62; Ian Hooten/ Mother And Baby Picture Library p76; Image Source Pink/Alamy p67; Itani/ Alamy p8; Jaimie D Travis/DK Stock/Getty Images p134; Jennie Woodcock/Reflections Photolibrary/Corbis p162; Jim Pickerell/ Rex Featuresp145; Juice Images/Imagestate p129; Jupiter Images/Polka Dot/Alamy p167; JUPITERIMAGES/BananaStock/Alamy p34; JUPITERIMAGES/Polka Dot/Alamy p86; Kei Uesugi/Taxi/Getty Images p78; Losevsky Pavel/Shutterstock p99; Masterfile p98; Matka Wariatka/Shutterstock p182; Nicole Hill/ Rubberball/Getty Images p38; numb/Alamy p11; Pearson Education Ltd p44; Pearson Education Ltd/Bananastock p2; Pearson Education Ltd/Ben Nicholson p99; Pearson Education Ltd/Clark Wiseman p50; Pearson Education Ltd/Creatas p43; Pearson Education Ltd/Gareth Boden p118; Pearson Education Ltd/Ian Wedgewood p22; Pearson Education Ltd/ Jules Selmes pp6, 19, 20, 38, 38, 39, 39, 39, 40, 40, 40, 40, 43, 81, 96, 102, 107, 111, 113, 133, 138, 139, 142, 143, 146, 151, 158, 162, 171, 176, 187; Pearson Education Ltd/Jules Selmes/Courtesy of Middlesex New (Reform) Synagogue, Harrow. p10; Pearson Education Ltd/Lisa Payne Photography pp133, 154, 156; Pearson Education Ltd/Lord and Leverett p33; Pearson Education Ltd/Photodisc p96; Pearson Education Ltd/Studio 8/Clark Wiseman p85; Pearson Education Ltd/ Tudor Photography pp11, 72, 122; Peter Hendrie/The Image Bank/Getty Images p108; Radius Images/Alamy p60; Raith/Mauritius/Photolibrary.com p136; RapidEye/istockphoto.com pp97, 99; Sally & Richard Greenhill/Alamy p10; Sharon Dominick/Photodisc/Getty Images p126; Somos Images/Corbis p17; Stockbyte/SW Productions/Getty Images p27; Studio 10 - Scholastic/Index Stock Imagery/Photolibrary.com p155; Tetra Images/Alamy p99; tiburonstudios/Istockphoto p99; Vaidas Bucys/Shutterstock p37; Woodystock/Alamy p97

Every effort has been made to contact copyright holders of material reproduced in this book. Any omissions will be rectified in subsequent printings if notice is given to the publishers.

Contents

Introduction

Who is this book for?

This book has been specially written to support the CACHE Foundation Award in Caring for Children, although it will also be helpful for students studying similar introductory courses in childcare and education. The CACHE Foundation Award in Caring for Children provides the opportunity to develop basic skills in caring for children. The book takes you step by step through the learning topics in the syllabus and provides support with the portfolio assessments in it.

Features of this book

- This book has **seven units** to match the units of the CACHE Foundation Award in Caring for Children.
- Each **unit** is split into a number of **learning topics** which take you through the things you need to know.

The seven units cover the learning topics on double-page spreads, which include the following features, designed to make the information clear and easy to find.

At the beginning of a topic is the following feature:

- **In the real world** which explains how you will be able to apply the knowledge you will learn to a real-life situation.

In the main pages of a topic you will find the following features:

- **Activities** to help you develop your understanding of the topic.

- **Case studies** describe situations to help you relate what you have learned to the real world. They may be followed by a question to help you reflect on the importance of what you have learned.

- **Summaries** to help you remember the key points. They will also help you revise information ready for the end-of-course test.

At the end of each unit, you will find a combination of the following features:

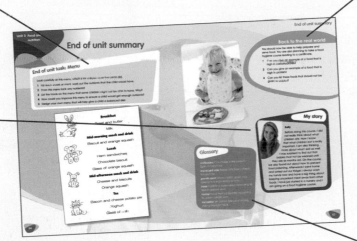

- **End of unit tasks** help you to practise the study skills you will need for your portfolio tasks.

- **My story** in which a student tells their own story of a real-life situation relating to one of the topics in the unit.

- **Back to the real world** will help you to check whether you have understood the essential information in the unit, by asking you some practical questions.

- **Getting ready for assessment** provides information which will help you to prepare for your assessment.

- **Glossary** gives definitions of some of the more difficult words used in that unit.

A note from the author

Working with children is interesting, tiring but also fun! There are many jobs open to people who have childcare qualifications and the course you are starting will be a good introduction to the world of childcare, education and play work.

Most people find that beginning a new course can be daunting. There are skills to be gained and knowledge to be learned. Finishing the course may seem a long way ahead! In writing this book, I hope that I will be able to help you on your 'learning journey'.

Good luck with your course!

Penny Tassoni

Unit 1 Personal development

Adults working with children have to be responsible and able to take care of themselves as well as the children. They also need to be able to work as part of a team and understand how to value and respect others.

This unit introduces you to some of the knowledge and skills you will need when working in childcare settings. The topics you will find in this unit are:

- Citizens and society
- Different cultures, beliefs and values
- Learning about others
- The principles of diversity and inclusive practice
- Finding a job
- Job applications and interviews
- Personal health issues
- Time management and teamwork
- Evaluating your work and making action plans

- How to work well in a childcare setting
- Basic skills for communicating with children and adults
- Hygiene, safety and confidentiality at work
- Good personal hygiene

At the end of this unit, your tutor has to write a report on you. You will need to demonstrate many of the skills and qualities that are required in adults who work with children. You will have an opportunity to show that you have developed these skills while on placement and also in class.

In the real world

It is your first day on this course and you are feeling quite nervous. You are not sure what you are going to do when the course ends. You have heard that you will be learning about inclusive practice. You are not sure what this means and what it has to do with working with children.

By the end of this unit, you will have taken your first steps towards working with children and other adults. You will know what inclusive practice means and how it affects the way that you work with children. You will also have learned some useful tips about applying for jobs or training courses and coping with an interview process.

Citizens and society

Children learn from the adults they are with. This means adults working with children must be responsible citizens. So what does being a responsible citizen mean?

Being a responsible citizen

We do not live completely by ourselves. We live in a society where people have to share roads, shops and services like gas and water. For society to work properly there are laws and **regulations**. Laws are used by society to make sure everyone knows what is expected of them. For example, parents know it is the law for their children to be **educated** between the ages of five and sixteen. Laws only work if most people follow them. Being a responsible citizen means obeying the laws.

Changing the laws or regulations

So where do the laws come from? The laws are passed by the United Kingdom's parliament in London, the Welsh Assembly and parliaments in Scotland and Northern Ireland.

Who makes the laws?

Members of Parliament (MPs) vote on laws that are put forward. There is an MP for each area of the country. Do you know the name of your local MP?

How do people change the law?

People can tell their MP if they think a law is unfair. They can also vote for a different MP in an election. Most citizens over the age of 18 can vote in an election. Voting gives us a say in our society.

These boys are learning to take turns. How will this help them in later life?

Issues facing society

Our society has some problems. Some of the problems are hard to solve and people have different ideas about solving them.

Responsible citizens care about what happens to others. Some of the money that the government receives from taxes is spent on caring for other citizens.

Poverty

Some people and families are poor. They may have enough money for food and shelter, but not enough **income** to buy clothes or to heat their homes. There are many groups of people living in poverty. They include some elderly people, people with no jobs and families who are on low incomes. People who are poor are more likely to become ill. Look at the ways in which poverty can affect children.

Health
- Children may be too hungry or tired to concentrate.
- Children are more likely to be ill.
- Children are more likely to have accidents.

Poverty and children

Confidence
- Children may feel that they are different from other children.

Education
- Children from poor homes may do less well at school.
- Children may not have books and toys at home.

Unemployment

There are times when **unemployment** in our society is very high. This means it is hard to find a job. Being unemployed often means living in poverty. It makes people feel depressed and often angry.

Homelessness

There are many reasons why people do not have homes. Some are young people who have run away. Others are people who are on drugs or abuse alcohol. Homeless people may live on the streets or in hostels. Some people who are homeless feel that society does not care about them. People who are homeless can be in danger; they may also become ill.

Drug abuse

Drugs change people's behaviour and way of thinking. This means that adults who are using drugs should not work with children. Although drugs are **illegal**, they are still a problem in our society. Many drugs are **addictive**, which means that people find it hard to stop taking them. Parents who use drugs often find it harder to care for their children.

Activity

People have different ideas about what being a responsible citizen means.

1 With a partner, think of three or four things that you think being a responsible citizen means.

2 Compare your ideas with the other people in your class.

Summary

- Adults working with children need to be responsible citizens.
- Responsible citizens obey the law and care about their society.
- Some issues facing our society are poverty, homelessness and drug abuse.

Different cultures, beliefs and values

We are lucky to live in a society where people can have different ideas and beliefs. This means that some people may have a different way of living from your own (a different lifestyle).

Some ways in which people may be different include:

● language
● food
● drink
● clothing
● places of worship
● ideas about relationships
● homes
● festivals
● sense of humour.

Why do I need to find out about others' beliefs and lifestyles?

When working with children and their families, you need to know about the way they live and about their beliefs. This helps you to understand their needs better.

▲ Fatima is **bilingual**. She speaks one language at home and a different one at nursery. (People who can speak three languages or more are called **multilingual**.) Adults working with Fatima need to find out about her home language.

▲ Ahmed's family is observing the Islamic holy month of Ramadan. Adults eat only before dawn and after sunset. When it is time to eat, everyone celebrates. It is important for adults working with Ahmed to find out how he will be joining in during Ramadan.

Understanding our own values and beliefs

Every person has their own values and beliefs. People usually have similar values and beliefs to their families and friends. If people are surrounded by others who share the same beliefs and values, they can sometimes forget that others have different values and beliefs.

On the next page you will be able to read about the values and beliefs of certain groups of people.

Case study

Shona, a nursery assistant, has found out that a child's family is Jewish. One lunchtime she stops the child from having a yoghurt for pudding because she thinks that Jews do not have dairy foods if meat has been served. The child cries. The parents are cross. They explain that they are Jewish but they do not follow all the dietary restrictions.

Why is it important to find out directly from parents about their child's needs?

On the next page you will be able to read about some of the values and beliefs of Jewish people.

Activity

With a partner, talk about your answers to the questions below and then share your answers with others in your group.

1 What festivals do you celebrate?

2 How do you celebrate them?

3 Do you celebrate birthdays?

4 Are there any special foods that you eat during a festival?

5 Are there any foods that you do not eat?

6 How does your family celebrate the birth of a child?

7 Who do you live with?

8 Do you speak more than one language?

9 Do you go to a chapel, church, temple, synagogue or other place of worship?

10 Do you think that swearing is wrong?

Summary

- Everyone has values and beliefs.
- We must remember that not everyone will share our beliefs and values.
- We must respect others' values and beliefs even if they are different from our own.
- It is important to learn about the beliefs and values of the families we are working with.

Learning about others

It is also useful to learn about common beliefs and practices held by large numbers of people in our society. The information below might help you to learn more about some groups of people. It is important, though, to remember that this is only general information and that each family may have their own ways.

Jews

Jews practise a religion called **Judaism**. They visit synagogues to worship. Many Jews will not work on Saturdays as this is their day of worship and rest. Jews also follow strict food laws for their religion (see also page 80) which include not eating pork.

Sikhs

Sikhs practise a religion called **Sikhism**. They believe in not cutting their hair. The men and boys wear turbans because they believe they are not complete without one. Sikhs pray at a temple.

Muslims

Muslims practise a religion called **Islam**. They try to pray five times a day. They also visit mosques to worship. Muslims follow the food laws of their religion (see also page 80) which include not eating pork and not drinking alcohol. Keeping clean is also important for Muslims and they try to wash under running water.

Hindus

Hindus practise a religion called **Hinduism**. They visit Mandirs to worship and at home they worship at a shrine. They believe in reincarnation: the idea of being reborn.

Christians

Christians practise a religion called **Christianity**. They go to churches or chapels to worship. There are different groups of Christians including Catholics, Protestants, Seventh Day Adventists and Mormons. Christian groups celebrate the life and death of Jesus.

Other groups

Travellers

There are different groups of travellers. The oldest groups of travellers are gypsies. Their families have been travelling around Europe for hundreds of years and they have their own language called **Romany**. Travellers want to feel they are free to move around rather than living in just one place.

Vegetarians and vegans

People may be vegetarian or vegan for many reasons. It may be part of their religion or they may not like the idea of killing animals.

Vegetarians do not eat meat or fish, but will often eat eggs, milk, cheese and other dairy products

Vegans do not eat any food or drink that comes from animals or fish. Many vegans do not use or wear anything that comes from killing animals – e.g. leather.

Activity

Choose one of the groups of people described in the boxes. Use the Internet to find out more about their beliefs and needs. Create a leaflet that would help an early years worker understand more about this group.

Summary

- It is important to have some knowledge about common beliefs.
- It is useful to find out directly from parents about their beliefs.
- Many people may have food preferences linked to their beliefs.

The principles of diversity and inclusive practice

Most people want to be treated fairly and with respect. They want to be given the same chances as others and get help when they need it. It is the right of every individual, including children, to be treated fairly and with respect, whatever their background, culture or physical appearance.

What is diversity?

The term 'diversity' is used to help people remember that we live in a society where we all have different approaches to living our lives.

What is inclusive practice?

Inclusive practice means finding ways of making sure that every child and their family feel welcome. It also means that children are given the encouragement they need to do as well as they can.

The word **discrimination** is used when people are not being treated fairly.

The diagram shows some groups of people that are commonly discriminated against in the UK.

People are treated unfairly in many ways. They may be turned down for jobs or **promotion**. They may be refused entry to places or may be given poor service in shops. They may be kept waiting in offices or be spoken to rudely. Children can be discriminated against too. For example, they may not get the same help and time from adults because they come from a poor home or single-parent family.

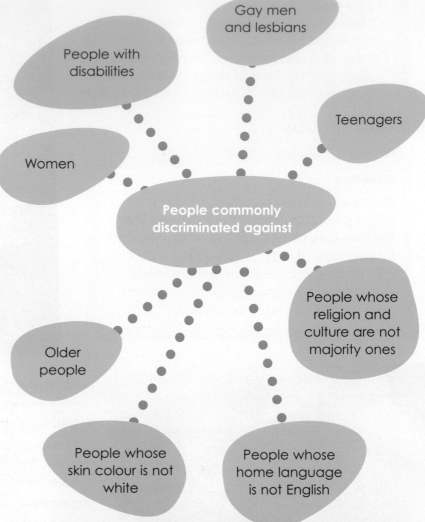

People with disabilities

Gay men and lesbians

Teenagers

Women

People commonly discriminated against

People whose religion and culture are not majority ones

Older people

People whose skin colour is not white

People whose home language is not English

All children should have the right to play and learn. Why do you think this is important?

Changing our society

No one likes feeling they are being treated badly. There are laws that help protect people from discrimination. Laws can help stop discrimination but, to make a fairer society, people's attitudes need to change as well.

People working with children can help with this because they are working with the next generation. They can help children learn to respect and help others.

How to make a difference

Make children feel welcome and valued.	Smile and greet children.
Respect children's culture and religious beliefs.	Find out from their parents about the food they need and the language they speak.
Do not have favourite children.	Spend time with every child.
Help children to find out that there are many languages, cultures and religions.	Play nursery rhyme CDs in other languages. Have a good choice of dressing-up clothes.
Help children learn about other cultures.	Use activities such as cooking, making masks, playing games from other cultures and celebrating festivals.

Showing inclusive practice

Inclusive practice means making sure every child we work with gets the attention and support he or she needs. **It does not mean treating every child exactly the same**. This would not help those children who need extra support or equipment.

There are many ways adults can help children feel valued. We also need to help them learn about and respect others.

Activity 1

Look at the following examples and think about how the children might feel.

1 The nursery is making Mothers' Day cards. David lives in a children's home. He is told not to bother making one.

2 The after-school club is organising a visit to a theme park. The children are asked to bring in £12.50. Kyle's mum says he cannot go because it is too much money.

3 Suantha has the use of one arm. She is told that there is no point in trying to play netball.

Activity 2

Answer the following questions:

1 What does discrimination mean?

2 What does inclusive practice mean?

3 Why do people working with children need to think about the activities that they are planning?

Summary

- Several groups of people are discriminated against in our society.
- Adults must make sure that children are given equal opportunities to play and learn.
- Inclusive practice does **not** mean treating every child the same.
- Adults working with children must make sure that their actions and any activities they plan do not discriminate against any children.

Finding a job!

Finding a job is a skill. You need to know what type of job you want and how to find it.

Understanding the jargon!

A good starting point is to understand the words used by employers. See if you can match the **words** with the **descriptions**. The first one has been done for you.

Words	Descriptions
Curriculum vitae (CV)	Someone who can give your employer more information about you. They should know you well (e.g. a teacher, lecturer or someone you have worked for). By talking or writing to your employer they are giving you a reference.
References	To put yourself forward for a job.
Salary	A summary of your skills, work experience and personal details that helps the employer to find out about you.
Referee	Someone who works for an employer.
Job description	
Employer	Extra information about you that the employer gets from writing or talking to your referee (someone you have suggested).
Employee	Details of what you would be expected to do.
Apply	Someone who pays people to work for them.
Application form	The date by which you have to have applied for the job.
Closing date	The amount you will be paid over a year.
	A form that an employer wants you to fill in.

Spot the jargon!
Look at these two job advertisements. Can you find the jargon words?

Blackstone Out-of-School Club

We are looking for part-time staff to work in our growing club.

- Excellent working conditions
- Salary: £14,000–£16,000 according to experience

Please send in a letter of application with CV and names of referees to:

Mr A Mitchell, Blackstone Out-of-School Club, Southmead Road, Blackstone BR4 8KL

Early Years Nursery, Kingston

We are seeking qualified and unqualified employees to work in our popular nursery.

Minimum salary:
£15,000

Phone 01838 783999 for an application form and full job description.
Closing date for applications 25 June

Getting ready to apply for a job

Before starting to look for jobs, you must do some preparation. Look at the following steps.

1 Make sure the information you have is up to date.

Find documents you could show an employer such as:
- National Record of Achievement
- portfolios of coursework and evidence
- certificates such as first aid, GCSE, life saving
- reports.

2 Ask people you know if they will be referees.

Most employers want to talk to or write to someone who has seen you work or who knows you well. You will need to ask two or three people if they will be happy to give you a reference. They should be people who will have good things to say about you!

3 Write a CV.

Most CVs have the following sections:
- Personal details: name, date of birth, address, phone number.
- Education and qualifications: a list of courses or qualifications that you have done. You should give dates and places.
- Work experience: a list of jobs or placements that you have had, with dates. You can briefly describe what you did.
- Other interests: a list of activities that you do in your free time.
- Referees: the names and addresses of two people who can give more information to your employer. You should ask them first if they are happy to do this for you.

4 Look for a job.

Once you have finished your CV, you will need to start looking for a job. There are several places where you might find a job, including:
- newspapers
- job centres
- schools/nurseries
- Internet job websites
- magazines
- nanny/au pair agencies
- local careers service.

The golden rules of job hunting are:

1 Follow the instructions in the advertisement carefully.
2 Apply quickly.
3 Make sure your CV and letter of application suit the job for which you are applying.

Activity

Choose the correct word to fit the description:

1 You fill one in to apply for a job.
A _ _ _ _ _ _ _ _ _ _ F _ _ _
2 This tells employers about your skills and qualifications. C _
3 These people will be contacted by an employer to find out more about you. R _ _ _ _ _ _ _
4 This tells you when the employer needs to receive your application by.
C _ _ _ _ _ _ D _ _ _
5 This gives you more information about the job.
J _ _ D _ _ _ _ _ _ _ _ _ _

Summary

- It is important to keep certificates and records of achievement safe.
- Many employers will ask for a CV (curriculum vitae).
- Most employers will ask you for the names of two referees.

Job applications and interviews

Once you have seen a job or a training course, the next steps are to find out more about it and then to apply. You may then be offered an interview.

Phoning about a job or training course

Some adverts ask you to make a phone call. It is a good idea to choose a quiet place to make the call. Think through what you need to say before you call:

- Have a pen and paper ready in case you need to write down any information.
- Make sure that you speak in a clear voice.
- Be ready to ask questions – for example, where the job is or how long the training course lasts.
- Don't forget to give your name and address so that an application form or more information can be sent to you.

Filling in an application form

Make sure you read all the instructions and questions carefully. You should fill in the form neatly and make sure that the information is accurate. A good tip is to write in pencil first or to take a photocopy of the form to practise on. Ask someone to check your rough version before you copy it out neatly. Always keep a copy of the application form so you can read through it before an interview.

Writing a letter of application

Some jobs ask for a letter of application. If you are already sending in an application form or a CV, this may be quite a short letter. The letter of application is a way of 'selling' your skills and talents. Think about the things that will make you a good person to give this job to. Always keep a copy of your letters of application so you can read through them before an interview.

37 Eastern Road
Coaxworth
Kent
CX25 7HY

Dear mrs BLake,

I am writing to apply for the post of classroom assistant that I saw advertised in the paper

I have just finished a course and I feel I am ready to take on the responsibility of a classroom assistant.

i have had training that included working along side a teacher and children aged between 5 and 7 and get on well with children and class techers.

I have enjoyed my training throughly and I hope I have the reliability and still that is required in your school.

I enclose my CV which I hope is helpful.

Yours sincerely

Stephanie Butchers
Stephanie Butchers

This letter of application is quite good, but there are some mistakes. Can you find them?

Getting ready for an interview

Most people get nervous before an interview. It helps if you prepare yourself beforehand. You should read through your CV, letter of application and/or application form. This will remind you what you have said about yourself.

Before the day

- Find out how to get there.
- Plan what you will wear and make sure it's clean and ironed.
- Think about what you can take with you to show the interviewers.
- Find out more about the job/ training course if you can.
- Practise some interview questions with a friend or tutor.

On the day

- Make sure that you look smart, clean and tidy.
- Set off in plenty of time.
- Phone if you are going to be late.
- Try to arrive a few minutes early.
- If you are shown around the setting, make sure you look interested.

During the interview

- Smile as you walk in.
- Speak clearly.
- Look at the people asking questions.
- Listen carefully to the questions.
- Try to be keen.
- Shake hands and thank the interviewer(s) for inviting you.

After the interview

If you are applying for a training course, you are likely to be told whether the course is right for you straightaway. The person interviewing you may also suggest other courses that you could study. If you are applying for a job, you may not be told straightaway.

- Make sure that you can be contacted.
- If you are offered the job, make sure that you know when to start.
- If you are not offered the job, think about phoning to find out why.

Where can I get more help?

You can get advice about jobs from the employment service and also from the careers service where you are studying. Staff can help you with CVs, letters of application and also give you advice about job hunting.

Activity

Here are some questions that can help you to think about your skills and prepare for an interview. Think about what your answers would be and practise them with a friend, taking it in turns to be the interviewer.

1 Tell me about yourself.
2 Tell me about the course you are doing.
3 Why do you want to work here?
4 Tell me about your strengths and weaknesses.
5 Have you any particular skills?

▲ Try to smile during an interview.

Summary

- Always do what the advertisement asks.
- Find someone to check your CV and/or letter of application.
- Spend time preparing for an interview.

Personal health issues

Working with children is hard work and tiring. This is why it is important to keep healthy and fit.

Personal hygiene

Good personal hygiene is an important part of keeping healthy. You should pay regular attention to your hair, teeth, hands, feet and clothes.

Hair

Keep your hair neat. If you have long hair, then tie it back. When working with young children check your hair for head lice or nits. Head lice live on the scalp and lay eggs on the hair.

Teeth

Clean teeth are important to prevent bad breath. Drinking plenty of water and not smoking also helps to keep your breath fresh.

Clothes

Choose clothes that are practical. Make sure they are clean. Check with your setting if they have a style of dressing.

Hands

To avoid illness, hands need to be washed frequently in hot water with soap. Make sure you also dry your hands carefully. This stops germs from growing on the skin.
- Keep your nails short and clean.
- Wash and dry your hands after using the toilet.
- Wash and dry your hands before making or eating food.
- Wash and dry your hands after going outside.

Feet

Adults working with children are on their feet most of the day. This means that comfortable shoes that fit properly are essential. In some settings staff take off their shoes in baby rooms. This means that having clean feet is also important!

Smoking

It is not a good idea to smoke. Smokers are more likely to develop lung cancer and are also more likely to get coughs and colds than non-smokers. Some smokers also find that their breath smells. If you do smoke, try to stop smoking. **You should never smoke in front of children.** The smoke can trigger asthma attacks in children.

Drug and alcohol abuse

To work with children you need a clear mind. You must be able to think and move quickly. Drugs and alcohol change the way people think and act. They can stay in the body for hours after they have been used. **If you are taking drugs or drinking lots of alcohol, you should not be working with children as you may not be able to keep them safe.** If you are taking prescription drugs that make you sleepy or have other side effects, you must tell your placement supervisor.

Sleep

Working with children can be very tiring. Sleep is one way for the body to fight infections. This means that having enough sleep is essential. Most people need around eight hours a night. If you have not slept enough, it is much harder to be interested in children and to control your moods.

▲ Why is it important to keep fit and healthy when working with children?

Diet

Food provides us with energy and also other nutrients that the body needs. If you do not eat properly, you are more likely to be off sick. On pages 62–63 we look at what makes a diet healthy. It is a good idea to eat sensible meals and to avoid having too many sugary or fatty snacks.

Exercise

Exercise can help our bodies to stay in shape. Some regular exercise, even if it is only walking, can help our bodies to fight off infection and stay strong.

Activity

Sue Lobb wants to be a childcare worker but she is always tired. She often takes days off because she is ill. She smokes 20 cigarettes a day, drinks heavily and rarely eats properly.

1 Working in pairs, think of five key pieces of advice you could give to Sue.

2 Role play what you would say to her, with one of you playing Sue.

Summary

- Working with children is demanding and tiring.
- Adults need to be fit and healthy to work with young children.
- Good personal hygiene can help us stay healthy.
- Healthy food, rest and exercise are ways of keeping healthy.
- Adults should not smoke in front of children.
- Adults who are on drugs or who are abusing alcohol should not work with children.

Time management and teamwork

Time management is about being able to use the time you have well. This is important because there are many tasks that need doing in early years and other settings. Students also need to be able to use their time well so that they can complete their work and meet any deadlines that they have been set.

Tips for good time management

- Work out exactly what needs doing – can it be broken into smaller tasks?
- Work out how long each task will take.
- Set out times when tasks can be done.
- Make sure you use this time.

Manjit works part-time after college. She knows she will not have a whole hour to do her work. Look at the flow chart at the bottom of the page to see how she worked out when and how she was going to do an activity from her textbook.

▲ Good time management is essential in an early years setting. This includes tidying toys at regular intervals.

Read the task through

On the bus going home

10 mins

Get out paper and do task in rough

Before starting work

20 mins

Read task and make changes

After work

10 mins

Write out neatly

Next day at lunchtime in college

20 mins

How to become a valued team member

Many adults working with children are part of a team. In some settings, like small play groups, teams might be quite small with four or five members. In other settings, like schools, the teams might be larger with 20 or more members. For teams to work well together, each member must do their share of the work and be ready to help out others. A good team member always puts the needs of the children and the team first.

The things you need to do to be an effective team member include:

- ✔ Follow instructions carefully.
- ✔ Work hard and skilfully.
- ✔ Be on time.
- ✔ Ask for help.
- ✔ Look for ways of helping other team members.
- ✔ Be cheerful.
- ✔ Avoid gossiping.
- ✔ Keep confidentiality (see also page 29).
- ✔ Share ideas.
- ✔ Be ready to do a little more than necessary to help out.

How teamwork helps children

When a team is working well together, everyone benefits. Look at some of the benefits of good teamwork.

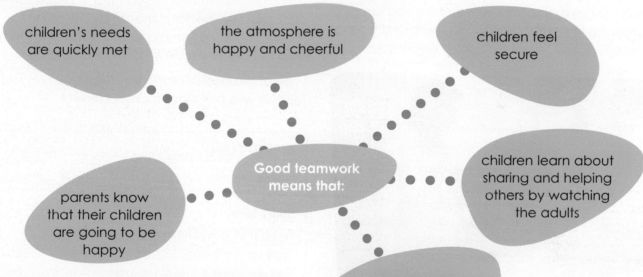

children's needs are quickly met

the atmosphere is happy and cheerful

children feel secure

parents know that their children are going to be happy

Good teamwork means that:

children learn about sharing and helping others by watching the adults

team members enjoy coming to work

Activity

Here are some of the tasks that need doing in many early years settings:
- setting up the home corner
- clearing away the dough table
- putting out paints
- tidying up the sand and water areas.

1 Working with a partner, choose two tasks.

2 Work out what needs to be done for each.

3 Work out how long it will take.

Summary

- Time management is about using your time well.
- It helps if you set out times for doing different tasks and stick to them.
- Most people who work with children are part of a team.
- Team members put the needs of the children and the team first.
- Good team members are ready to do a little more than necessary.

Evaluating your work and making action plans

Working with children requires skills. To improve your skills with children, you need to think about how well you are doing. This will help you to think about how to improve. It will also help you think about your future career.

Listening to others

Evaluating your work means thinking about how well you are doing. Your tutors and placement supervisors will probably tell you how you are doing. It is important to listen to them and work to improve skills where you have weaknesses.

▲ Your supervisor can give you useful feedback on your work. Make sure you listen and take in what your supervisor tells you.

Evaluating your own work

The best person to evaluate your work is you! If you can see your own strengths and weaknesses, you will find it easier to work effectively. You need to think honestly about how you have worked and also watch the reactions of children and staff while you are working.

Using action plans and making decisions

An action plan helps you focus on the things you need to do next. It can also help you think about your career. When drawing up an action plan, you need to make some decisions. You have to decide what needs doing and how long it will take.

To check your progress, you need to look at your action plan and maybe put in place some changes. This is what is meant by the term 'reviewing an action plan'. Your tutor may be able to help you review your action plan.

Look at the action plan that Heather is using after the talk with her placement supervisor.

ACTION PLAN

NAME Heather Wilson   **DATE** 20th June

Short term
Finish Unit 2 assignment
Copy up notes from 16th June
Find out about a first aid course
Find out how to use the computer

Medium term
Complete first aid course
Finish college course
Start computer course

Goals for the future
Move on to Diploma course
Find work in a nursery

SIGNED   H. Wilson

Career choices and training

There are many careers available to people working with children. The chart below shows some of the jobs that you may wish to aim for in the future, although for most you will need further training. Towards the end of your course your tutor or careers adviser can help by telling you more about the jobs that are available and also the training and qualifications that you would need to have.

Job	Job role
Teaching assistant	Helps teacher in the class
Midday supervisor	Looks after children in schools at lunchtimes
Early years teacher	Teaches young children in nurseries or schools
Nursery assistant	Works in a nursery alongside others
Play group assistant	Works in a play group alongside others
Crèche worker	Works in a crèche, where children do not stay for long periods of time
Nanny	Works alone in a family home looking after children
Au pair	Works in a foreign country and helps look after children in a family home while learning the language
Holiday play scheme play worker	Looks after children in a holiday club
Holiday club play organiser	Organises play schemes during the holidays

Activity

Heather is getting feedback from her placement supervisor, Simi. Look at their conversation.

Simi: You seem to have settled in well, although you've been late in a couple of times.

Heather: Yes, sorry about that – I overslept, but I'm really enjoying it here.

Simi: That's good. Yesterday, I was pleased with the way you worked with Tony and Raj. They really enjoyed the game of dominoes. My only concern was that some of the other children wanted to join in and you didn't really pay much attention to them. Could you think about ways in which you can involve other children?

Heather: I suppose I could have got out other games, but I don't know where they're kept and I don't know the names of all the children.

Simi: Yes, you'll have to work a little harder on that, although you're very good at clearing and tidying away – which is a great help.

What are the strengths and weaknesses of this student?

Summary

- Evaluating your work helps you to improve your skills.
- An action plan is a way of deciding how to improve skills.
- Action plans may need to be changed or reviewed.
- Tutors and careers advisers can give information about careers working with children.

How to work well in a childcare setting

Working with children is a responsible job. Parents who leave their children with you need to know that you will look after them, be on time, be reliable and treat their children well. This means that punctuality, reliability, respect and courtesy are all important qualities in a childcare worker.

Punctuality

Punctuality is about being on time. Arriving late or taking longer than allowed for breaks lets others down. It might mean that parents cannot go off to work or that others in the team have to do more than their share of work. People who are frequently late cause bad feelings in teams.

Reliability

Being **reliable** means others can count on you. Adults working with children need to be reliable so that they do not let down children, parents and other team members. Being reliable helps with the smooth running of a childcare setting.

If you are going to be late, make sure you contact your work setting.

Make sure you have a reliable alarm clock.

Get to bed early enough.

How to be on time

Watch the clock during break and lunchtimes.

Allow extra time to get to work to allow for late buses or other problems.

Make sure you know exactly what you have to do.

If you are unwell and cannot go into work, contact your supervisor as soon as possible.

Tips for being reliable

Ask for help if you need it.

Always keep your promises.

If staff are reliable, then everyone knows that there will be enough staff to look after the children and that tasks like preparing activities, cleaning and clearing away will all be done properly. Children need reliable adults because they need security. They need to know that they can count on adults being there and that any promises adults have made will be kept. Children get very upset when they are let down or when there are many unexpected changes.

Respect and courtesy

Treating others with **respect** and **courtesy** helps everyone work well together. Children and their families need to be treated with respect and courtesy so they will feel welcome. Everyone is entitled to be treated with respect and courtesy. This includes children. When children are treated well, they feel wanted and secure. Children also learn a lot by simply watching how adults behave. They often copy adults' actions. This is called **role modelling**. When adults act as good role models by being pleasant and polite, children learn to treat others with respect and courtesy.

Greet and welcome parents and children.

Open doors for others.

Speak calmly and politely.

Showing respect and courtesy

Listen to others.

Remember to say 'please' and 'thank you'.

Offer to help out.

▲ Sonya knows that when she comes into nursery, there will always be someone she knows waiting to greet her. Why is this important?

Activity

Children need to hear adults saying 'please' and 'thank you' so they can copy them.

1 With a partner, think of five everyday opportunities when children might hear adults saying 'please' and 'thank you'.

2 Compare your ideas with other members of your group.

Summary

- Adults working with children need to be punctual and reliable.
- It is important to let others know if you cannot go into work.
- Everyone is entitled to respect and courtesy.
- Children learn how to respect others by watching adults.

Basic skills for communicating with children and adults

People who work with children and their families need to have good communication skills. These can help meet children's as well as their families' needs. Good communication skills are also needed in childcare setting to help teams work well.

There are many reasons why we need to be able to communicate with children and adults. Some of them are shown in the table to the right.

The basic skills of communication can be divided into four main areas (see below):

- body language and position
- speaking
- listening
- observing and thinking.

We need to communicate to:	For example:
Exchange information	'Simon was very late to bed last night.'
Socialise, build relationships and show feelings	'How are you feeling today?'
Give reassurance and comfort	'Don't worry, I'll stay here and I'll be here when you wake up.'
Explain	'We mustn't run here because we might fall and hurt ourselves.'

Body language and position are about the way we look when we are communicating. The way we stand, use our hands and make eye contact can all give the other person hidden messages. Our position can also send out messages – standing very close to someone can be threatening. Being too far away looks as if we're not interested.

Speaking is also an important part of communication. The way something is said is as important as the words. Our speech can also change depending on who we are with. Good communicators think about the words and expressions they use, make sure these are suitable, and show respect.

Listening is a skill. Listening to others means thinking about what they are saying and then responding. Good listeners show that they are listening by nodding, smiling and waiting for the speaker to finish. Good listeners also make comments and add questions that encourage speakers to carry on, such as: 'That sounded fun. Did you have a go too?'

It is important to **observe** and **think** while you're communicating. Good communicators listen carefully but also look at the other person's body language. They observe the effect of what they are saying on the other person. They make sure they are respectful and courteous.

How does this childcare worker's body language show that she wants to be with the child?

- She is looking at the child and making eye contact.
- Her facial expression is positive.
- Her hand movements show that she is explaining.
- Her position is good: she is near, but not too close to the child.

Helping children to talk to us

Some children find it hard to speak to adults. Using a toy or puppet can help them to relax. We can also help them by getting down to their height, smiling and making them feel that we will listen to what they are saying.

Do ...

✔ get down to children's height.
✔ give children plenty of time to speak.
✔ talk to children.
✔ show children you are listening.
✔ praise and respond to children.

Don't ...

✘ force children to say hello or to speak.
✘ finish off sentences for children.
✘ ignore what children are saying.

Activity 1

Sometimes we communicate by telephone.

Which of these speech bubbles would be the best one to use when talking to the parent of a child you are caring for? Give your reasons.

'Yeah, yeah. I suppose so. Look, I'll do that in a sec, when I've finished what I'm doing. Be seeing you then. Ta.'

'Yes, I see. I'll do that straight after I've finished taking the register. I look forward to seeing you later on. Thank you for phoning.'

Activity 2

With a partner take it in turns to actively listen to each other for a minute.

Summary

- Communication skills are important to help meet children's and their families' needs.
- Good communication also helps childcare settings run smoothly.
- It is important to listen, watch and think, as well as to speak, when communicating.

Hygiene, safety and confidentiality at work

We can keep children safe by making sure that they do not become ill. Children become ill because of germs. There are different types of germs. Some are called **bacteria** and some are called **viruses**. Germs can be found in the air and also on our hands and in our food. **Basic hygiene** is about stopping the germs from spreading and reaching children.

One way to stop germs from spreading is by washing our hands. Germs are often on hands and are spread when we touch toys and equipment. Hands should be washed with warm water and soap. They need to be carefully dried too. We also need to make sure that children wash their hands.

Wash hands after doing a messy activity.

Wash hands after using the toilet.

Wash hands before touching or eating food.

Wash hands after playing outside.

Wash hands after blowing a nose.

Wash hands after touching animals.

▲ Can you think of some other examples of when to wash your hands?

Safety

Accidents happen very quickly. Adults working with children need to watch and think all the time.

Watch carefully.	If you see children arguing or playing dangerously, step in.
Tidy up.	Make sure toys are not left lying around. Dangerous things like cleaning fluids should be safely stored away.
Check for hazards.	Make sure toys and equipment are not damaged or broken. Look out for toys that are unsuitable for children.
Use safety equipment.	Make sure you know how to use equipment such as stair gates safely.

Confidentiality

People who work with children find out a lot of information about them and their needs. Very often this information is useful because it helps the childcare worker to meet children's needs. For example, a child might be sad because her brother is ill or excited because he is going on holiday. If childcare workers know the reason, then they can respond well to the child. However, we may find out information about the children, their families, or even other members of staff, which they do not want other people to know. This information is confidential and must not be passed on.

Talking to parents about their children

Many parents want to find out about their children. They may ask you about them. At this point in your training, you should not be passing on information. You will need to find another member of staff who is responsible for the child.

I've just come to let you know that I'm splitting up with my husband. Anna may be a bit upset

Thank you for letting me know. I'll keep an eye on Anna

▲ Why would this be confidential information? Why is it useful for the staff working with Anna to know this?

Activity

Look at the picture of a nursery below.

1 Find the three hazards in the picture.

2 With a partner, discuss what you would do about each of the three hazards.

Summary

- Children rely on adults to keep them safe.
- Good hygiene prevents infections.
- Information that you learn about children and their families is usually confidential.
- Breaking confidentiality is the same as breaking someone's trust in you.
- Always check whether you can pass on information if you are unsure.

Good personal hygiene

Personal hygiene is about keeping our bodies and clothing clean. Good personal hygiene is essential for everyone who works with children.

We need to keep clean in order to:
- prevent germs from spreading from us to others
- prevent germs from entering our bodies
- prevent us from smelling
- make us feel good
- make us look better.

Keep your hair neat – if you have long hair, tie it back.

Always wear clean underwear.

Wear little or no jewellery.

Wear flat-soled, non-slip shoes.

Tips for personal hygiene

Keep your nails short and clean.

Change your socks (or tights) daily.

Clean your teeth twice a day.

Wear comfortable clothing that can be easily washed – e.g. a tracksuit.

Jewellery

Avoid jewellery, especially earrings. These can get caught in clothing or be pulled out by babies! Bacteria can also hide in jewellery.

Skin

The body uses skin to help control its temperature. When it is hot, sweat is produced to cool down the body. Keeping skin clean is very important. Skin acts as a barrier between the outside and inside of our bodies. It stops some germs getting inside our bodies and causing infection. The easiest way to keep skin clean is to shower or bathe every day. This removes dead cells.

Hands and nails

The skin on our hands must be kept clean. Bacteria can reach our hands easily, as we use them constantly. Bacteria are easily spread from hands to objects like toys and food. This means that adults who work with children must wash their hands frequently during the day and before touching babies. It is also important to keep nails clean and short, as bacteria can collect under them. Most settings do not allow staff to wear nail varnish, especially if they handle food.

On page 28 we looked at the importance of hand washing at certain times of the day. Write down five times in the day when hands must be washed. Look back at page 28 and check your answers.

Covering cuts and blisters

When working with children, any damage to our skin needs covering. This stops germs getting in and spreading to children. Covering up cuts is essential, especially when working with food.

Did you know?

Blue plasters are often used in kitchens so that they can be easily seen if they fall into food!

Hair

Hair needs brushing or combing every day. It is a good idea to tie back long hair so it does not touch children. This can help prevent head lice. Head lice are small insects that take blood from the scalp. They lay eggs that stick to the hair. The eggs (nits) are brown before they have hatched and white afterwards. Always tie back long hair when cooking.

Teeth

A smiling face is very attractive, but not if our breath is smelly! Bacteria in the mouth and on the teeth can cause bad breath. Cleaning our teeth stops bacteria building up on our teeth. Smoking also causes bad breath.

Clothing

It is important to wear clothes that are comfortable and sensible for working with children. It is essential to keep your clothes clean. Bacteria can build up on them so, even if you are clean, your clothes may still have bacteria on them. Clothes worn close to the skin, like underwear, need changing every day. Other clothing needs washing frequently.

Aprons

Many settings provide aprons for staff. Disposable aprons prevent bacteria reaching clothes. Always wear them when changing nappies and cleaning.

Acting as a role model for children

One of the ways children learn is by watching and copying adults. This type of learning is sometimes called **observational learning**. Adults who work with children need to be good **role models** so children can learn the importance of washing their hands and looking after themselves.

▲ Wash your hands alongside children.

- Make sure children see you wash your hands – e.g. before eating and after going outside.
- Wash your hands alongside children.
- Make sure you use soap and hot water and dry your hands carefully.
- Make sure children see you blow your nose and throw away the tissues.

Summary

- Good personal hygiene is about keeping our bodies and clothes clean.
- Good personal hygiene helps prevent the spread of germs.
- Children learn by watching adults.

Activity

Sarah is going to do a cooking activity with a group of children. She has a small cut on her hand.

1 With a partner, think of three things that she will need to do before starting this activity.

2 In your group, discuss why you made your choices.

End of unit summary

In this unit we looked at some of the skills and knowledge that adults who work with children need.

End of unit task 1: Skills

Copy out and complete the table to see how many skills you now have. Look for ways that you can show these skills – for example, reports, tutorial records, files, notes – or give examples of how you have shown these skills in practice. An example of how to fill in this table has been given.

Skill	How I can show this
I am punctual.	My timesheet shows that I am always on time for my placement.
I am reliable.	
I can use my time effectively – e.g. I am handing my coursework in on time and completing tasks in my placement.	
I am interested in learning.	
I am keeping information that might be useful when I apply for a job.	
I understand what inclusive practice means.	
I show respect and courtesy to others.	
I am able to listen to others, including children.	
I am able to communicate with children.	
I am able to follow instructions.	
I am able to keep information confidential.	
I am able to spot obvious hazards.	

End of unit task 2: Action plan

There may be some areas or skills that you still need to work on. Choose three skills that you still need to work on. Copy out and complete this table.

What I need to improve on	Reason	How I will do this
Punctuality	I am not always on time to my lessons.	I will wear a watch and stop talking to my other friends.

Back to the real world

You have successfully completed this unit. You now have an understanding of how to work with children and other adults. You also know how to apply for a job or cope with an interview. Best of all, you now know what 'inclusive practice' means and how that links to working with children.

1 Can you explain why it is important for people working with children to show inclusive practice?

2 Can you list three things that you must do to become a valued team member?

3 Can you explain why time management is so important?

Glossary

addictive Something that is hard to stop doing or taking

bilingual Able to speak two languages

discrimination Treating people differently

educated Taught

illegal Against the law

income Money to spend

multilingual Able to speak three or more languages

promotion Getting a better job

regulations Rules

role modelling Showing someone how to behave or act

unemployment Not having a job

My story

Michael

I did the CFCC course because I wanted to work with children. It really taught me about working with children and also other people. Before I started, I thought that working with children would be easy, but it is much harder than it looks. During the year, I learned about how to communicate with children, keep them safe, but also how to make sure that they were treated fairly. I think that I am more responsible now and more reliable. The skills we learned on this course enabled us to go on to do further training or to get a training post.

Unit 2 Human growth and development

Adults who work with children need to understand how children grow and develop. This helps them to plan activities and put out toys and equipment that will encourage the children's development. Children's needs change as they grow and develop, so adults also have to know about these and make sure they can meet them.

This unit looks closely at children's development and carries on to look at how a child becomes an adult and the events that shape people's lives.

The unit covers:

- the sequence of human growth and development from birth to old age
- factors and needs affecting a person's growth and development.

From this unit, you should be able to see that life has a pattern to it and that both children and adults have similar needs.

The topics you will find in this unit are:

- The principles of growth and development
- Babies: the first year
- Toddlers: one to three years
- Children: three to five years
- Children: five to eleven years – the primary years
- Eleven to eighteen years: adolescence
- Eighteen to fifty-five years: young adulthood into middle age
- Fifty-five years and over: late middle age into old age
- Factors affecting growth and development
- Language and communication skills
- Emotional and social needs

At the end of this unit, you should be able to understand how to meet the needs of children of different ages.

In the real world

You find out that you will be learning about how children and adults develop. You cannot see what learning about this has to do with working with children. You are afraid it is going to be boring.

By the end of this unit, you will know how babies and children develop and how this affects their later development. You will also have learned about how to stimulate babies and children.

The principles of growth and development

Babies and children grow and develop. Adults who work with children need to understand how children develop and grow so they can aid these processes.

The difference between growth and development

The word 'growth' is used to describe the way children's bodies get larger and heavier. Development is about the way children learn to use their bodies and gain skills. Children are regularly assessed for growth and development by health visitors and doctors to check that they are healthy.

Changes to body shape

As children grow, their body shape changes. Look at the diagram below. It shows how, as children get older, their legs and trunks make up more of the overall length of their bodies.

Development follows a sequence

Children develop skills at slightly different rates. Some babies can walk at 10 months; others at 15 months. Even though children do things at different rates, there is an order or sequence to development. This means that babies babble before they use words and children have to walk before they can run.

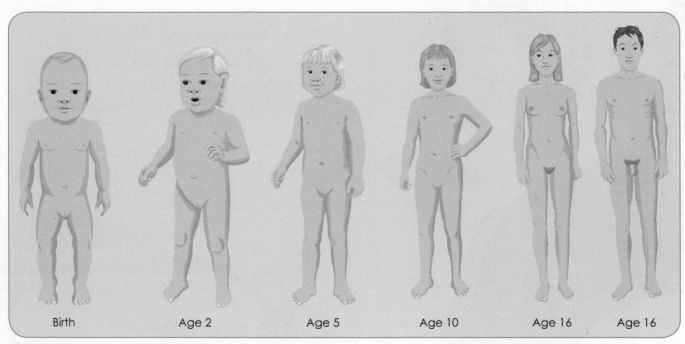

| Birth | Age 2 | Age 5 | Age 10 | Age 16 | Age 16 |

▲ Changes in body proportions from birth to adolescence.

Areas of development

Children's development is often divided into areas, although each area is linked to other areas. The areas of children's development are shown in the table below.

Measuring development

Adults who work with children look out for particular things, called milestones, for each area of development. For example, they may look to see if a child knows their colours or can climb upstairs by themselves.

▲ Completing a simple puzzle is an example of a milestone for intellectual development.

Area of development	Description
Physical	The process that helps children to learn to move and use their bodies – e.g. walking, throwing and catching.
Intellectual	The way children learn to think, use their memories and solve problems.
Language	The process that helps children learn to talk and listen to others or use sign language.
Social	The way children learn to play and work with other children and adults.
Emotional	The way children learn to express and control their feelings.

Activity

Reply to this letter written by a worried parent.

> Dear Janet,
>
> I am worried that my 13-month-old baby is not walking yet. My friend's baby walked when he was 12 months old.

Summary

- Health visitors and doctors regularly check children's growth and development.
- There are several areas of development.
- Development is measured by looking out for milestones.

Babies: the first year

The first year of life is one of much growth and development. At the end of this year, most babies are mobile, feeding themselves and beginning to communicate.

Learning to use their bodies: physical development

Babies are born with several actions or **reflexes** that they use to survive. They can cry, suck and grasp objects. By the end of the first year most babies are crawling or starting to walk. They can use their hands to feed themselves and hold and play with toys.

Learning to talk: communication skills

At first, babies can only communicate by crying but quickly begin to smile and study people's faces. They also begin to make babbling sounds.

By the end of the first year they can understand the meanings of many words. Babies' first words appear at around 13–15 months.

Learning to be with others: social and emotional development

Babies learn to trust special people in their lives. This process is called **attachment** or **bonding**. They may smile when they see them. By around eight months babies start to miss them and cry when left with strangers. Babies need special relationships to feel secure and know how to react to others. As well as needing people to feed and care for them, babies need adults to play with and talk to them. This is how they learn to communicate and use their developing physical skills. Playing, talking and singing to babies stimulates them.

Age	Stage of development	Toys	Activities to promote development
Newborn	• Reflexes – crying, sucking and grasping	• Mobiles • Brightly coloured toys	• provide plenty of physical contact • talk lovingly to babies • introduce household noises.
6 weeks	• Smiles and coos • Watches mother's or carer's face when fed	• Musical cot toys • Mobiles	• let them kick freely without a nappy on • talk to and smile with the baby • encourage laughter by tickling the baby.
3 months	• Starts to lift head when lying on stomach • Can hold a rattle for a few moments • Begins to babble	• Squeaky toys • Rattles • Baby gym • Activity blanket	• imitate the sounds made by the baby • sing nursery rhymes • encourage contact with other adults and children.

Age	Stage of development	Toys	Activities to promote development
6 months	• Begins to sit alone • Laughs and chuckles • Can pass toys from hand to hand	• Activity centres • Baby gym	• encourage movement by placing toys just out of baby's reach • look at picture books together • imitate animal sounds • provide cardboard boxes for the baby to put things into and take things out of.
9 months	• Sits up • Can often crawl or bottom shuffle • Picks up small objects using finger and thumb • Understands some words	• Peek-a-boo • Bricks • Bath toys • Stacking beakers • Toy telephone	• allow plenty of time for play • give them small, but safe, objects to pick up – always supervise • roll balls for baby to bring back to you • talk constantly.
12 months	• May be standing up by holding onto furniture • Points out objects • Drinks from a cup • Manages to eat finger foods such as toast and banana by themselves	• Brick trolley • Toy drum • Large ball	• read picture books with simple rhymes • play let's pretend games – e.g. pretend to be animals • talk about everyday activities – let baby respond.

Learning to think: cognitive development

Babies begin to develop concepts (ideas and thought patterns) from birth. For example, they will cry and make eye contact when they need something. Over their first year, they gradually develop new concepts. For example, they will repeat things they enjoy, like sucking their thumb. They will start to understand cause and effect and develop an understanding of objects. For example, if they are given a toy that squeaks, they will keep pressing it. By the end of the first year they will have developed the concept of trial and error – they will try different things to find out about an object. They will also understand the uses of familiar objects – for example, cuddling a teddy.

Activity

1 Name three skills that most babies have learned by nine months.
2 How do babies communicate?
3 Why do adults need to talk and play with babies?

Summary

• Babies are learning to control their bodies.
• Babies are learning how to be with others and to communicate.
• Babies need adults to talk and play with them.

Toddlers: one to three years

Toddler is the word used to describe children from the time they walk until they are around three years old. Working with toddlers is very rewarding but also hard work. Toddlers are busy little people who want constant adult attention! During this stage of their development they learn to speak, use the toilet, play and share with others. They also learn how to dress and feed themselves.

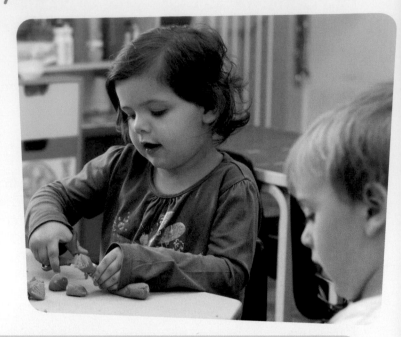

This chart shows what most toddlers are doing at different ages. Remember that all children develop at slightly different rates. These types of chart act only as a guide.

At eighteen months, most toddlers...

- say fifteen words
- point out objects to their carers
- can pull off their shoes
- can roll and throw a ball
- can walk downstairs with an adult
- cry when left with people they do not know.

At two years, most toddlers...

- put two words together to make a mini-sentence – e.g. 'cat gone'
- use a spoon to feed themselves
- can build a tower of five bricks
- play alongside other children
- want to be independent
- do not understand why they have to wait or cannot have things
- cry when left with people they do not know.

At three years, most toddlers...

- can talk quite well and use questions
- can walk and run confidently
- can draw a face
- can put on and take off their coat
- play with other children
- are out of nappies
- can be left with people they do not know for short periods of time
- can build a tower of nine or ten bricks.

Toddlers like to do things for themselves

It's hard to be a toddler. They can see things they want to do like doing up their shoes, but they don't have the skills to do it. They also see things they want but cannot have. They do not have enough language to explain what they want to do. This means they become frustrated and angry. Some toddlers show their anger and frustration by having tantrums. Adults working with toddlers try to think about situations that will trigger tantrums and then avoid them!

Safety

Toddlers are keen to explore and can move quickly. Many toddlers climb on furniture to reach objects that interest them. They have no sense of danger, yet try and copy adults' actions. This means that adults have to supervise them at all times and use safety equipment to prevent accidents.

Activity

Which of the following statements are true and which are false?

1 Most toddlers are out of nappies by eighteen months.

2 Toddlers should never be left alone.

3 Most two-year-olds can share toys.

4 At eighteen months most toddlers can be understood by strangers.

5 At three years, most toddlers can draw a face.

Summary

- Never leave a toddler alone.
- Toddlers are trying to be independent.
- Toddlers are learning to speak and play with others.

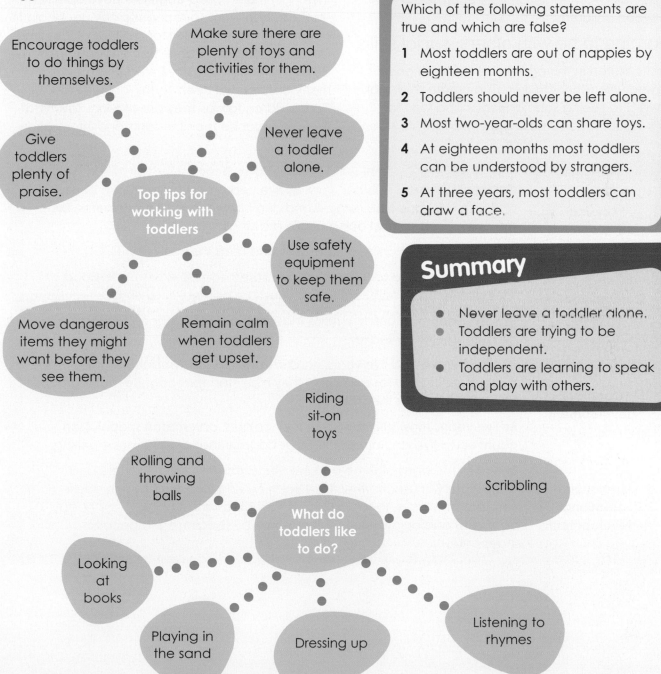

Encourage toddlers to do things by themselves.

Make sure there are plenty of toys and activities for them.

Give toddlers plenty of praise.

Never leave a toddler alone.

Top tips for working with toddlers

Use safety equipment to keep them safe.

Move dangerous items they might want before they see them.

Remain calm when toddlers get upset.

Riding sit-on toys

Rolling and throwing balls

Scribbling

What do toddlers like to do?

Looking at books

Playing in the sand

Dressing up

Listening to rhymes

Children: three to five years

Between the ages of three and five years, children become increasingly skilled and independent. During these years, they will start school, learn to play with others and begin to develop some of the skills they will need when they start to read and write.

Between the ages of three and five years, children's skills carry on developing. The rate of development can vary enormously between children.

Learning to be with others: social skills

Most children in this age group begin to enjoy playing with other children. They share toys, look forward to seeing special friends and start to think about others. These are important life skills.

Children also become more confident with other adults that they trust and are able to settle more easily with people they do not know.

Learning to think: cognitive development

Between the ages of three and five years, children begin to learn concepts or ways of thinking – this is called **cognitive development**. Most children learn to recognise colours, begin to count and start to understand a little about time. Children's language development and cognitive development are closely linked. This means that many children will need to think aloud. You will hear children talk as they are playing. Talk helps them to organise their thoughts and information.

Physical development	Children's physical skills can vary. By five years most children can bounce and catch a large ball, run well and also carry out small movements, like threading, cutting and doing simple drawings. At five years, most children can dress and feed themselves well.
Communication skills	Between three and four years, most children can be easily understood. They start to use whole sentences, questions and enjoy talking! By five years, most children have mastered speech, although they may still be making some mistakes.
Cognitive development	Between three and five years, children learn to use symbols – e.g. they may make a stick stand for a wand or they may start to recognise that a group of letters stands for their names. By five years, most children know their colours, can match shapes, can count up to five and are starting to recognise their own names in writing.
Social and emotional development	Between the ages of three and five years, children learn to share and cooperate with each other. They enjoy having friends, although adults find that they have to sort out some squabbles! Most children are happy, confident and enjoy helping others. They are beginning to become independent.

Activities for children aged three to five years

Children learn many things by playing. For example, they can learn about colours by painting, about money by playing 'shops' and about space and shape by playing with puzzles and bricks.

Children also learn about reading by sharing stories and rhymes with adults. They learn about writing through painting and drawing.

Look at the types of activities that most children of this age enjoy.

▲ Learning about writing through painting.

Top tips for working with three- to five-year-olds

- Make sure you keep an eye on them at all times.
- Provide a range of activities that will help them develop different skills.
- Read books and sing nursery rhymes to help children's language skills.
- Praise children when they are playing well together.
- Encourage children to dress and do things for themselves.

Activities for three- to five-year-olds

- Climbing frames, tricycles, hoops and balls
- Playing games like picture lotto or snap with an adult
- Dough and clay
- Train sets, farm animals
- Sand and water
- Dressing up clothes
- Puzzles and bricks
- Stories, rhymes and songs
- Painting and drawing

▲ Children at this age enjoy songs, rhymes and stories.

Activity

1 With a partner, think of a song or a game for a three- to five-year-old.

2 Talk about what they might learn from singing/playing it.

Summary

- By five years, most children can play with others.
- Children talk aloud to organise their thoughts.
- Children enjoy helping others and being independent.

Children: five to eleven years – the primary years

During these years, children's skills and knowledge continue to develop and they can apply them to new situations. By the age of eleven years, most children have mastered reading and writing and are able to think logically. The end of this period of development is marked by the first signs of puberty, when children's bodies begin to change.

Friendships are important

During this period, children start becoming more independent. They still need their families but often want to be with their peers (children of the same age). They have strong friendships and can play in groups. By seven years old, many children begin to compare themselves to their peers. They start to think about how well they are doing and may lose confidence. Some children who are not part of a friendship group may feel left out or may be bullied.

▲ Many children learn to swim at this age.

Physical development	During this period, children learn to balance, climb and use equipment such as bicycles and skateboards. Many children learn to swim and begin to play sports such as football, rounders and netball. Children's small movements also develop. By the age of eight, most children are able to write and join their letters. They also begin to enjoy activities that need good coordination such as model making, jigsaw puzzles, sewing and doing kits.
Communication skills	Children's speech carries on developing. By around six or seven years, they start to understand and enjoy jokes. By eleven years, they use language in many ways: to argue, protest, joke and give instructions. They can also read other people's body language and tone of voice. Between the ages of five and seven, children begin to learn to read and write and by eleven years have mastered the skills of reading and writing.
Cognitive development	In these years children's thinking develops. Children enjoy looking for rules and then using them – e.g. 'After Mary, its always Jo's turn.' At first, children learn by doing and by talking. They count using counters or objects. By seven years, most children are able to read, write basic sentences and do simple sums, although they will need to talk and think out loud. At eleven years, most children have mastered reading and writing, although they will still be making some mistakes.
Social and emotional development	By six to seven years, most children have good social skills. They are able to share, play and can understand others' points of view. By eleven years, most children understand right from wrong and can see that their actions and words may have consequences. Friends are very important to children from now on. Not having friends can make children very unhappy. Around nine to ten years, children start to judge themselves and may lose some confidence.

Children begin to have hobbies and join clubs

During this period, many children join clubs or have hobbies. Children make new friendships and also gain confidence by doing things in their spare time.

Did you do any of these popular activities as a child?

- Netball
- Playing the recorder
- Football
- Brownies or Cubs
- Dancing
- Swimming
- Table tennis
- Art club
- Trampolining
- Tai Kwando
- Judo
- Rugby
- Drama
- Skateboarding
- Rollerblading

Life at school

School life becomes very important for children. At school they learn to be part of a larger group of people and have to learn to work alongside others. Children also begin to notice if they cannot keep up with others in reading or maths. This can make them very unhappy.

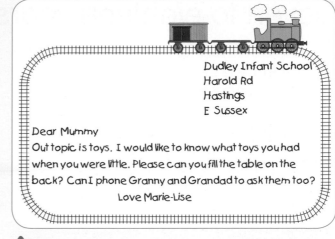

Dudley Infant School
Harold Rd
Hastings
E Sussex

Dear Mummy
Out topic is toys. I would like to know what toys you had when you were little. Please can you fill the table on the back? Can I phone Granny and Grandad to ask them too?
Love Marie-Lise

Most children make enormous progress in reading and writing between the ages of five and eleven years.

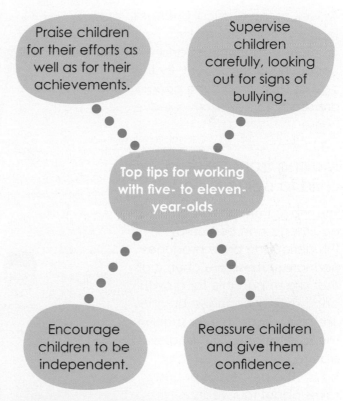

Praise children for their efforts as well as for their achievements.

Supervise children carefully, looking out for signs of bullying.

Top tips for working with five- to eleven-year-olds

Encourage children to be independent.

Reassure children and give them confidence.

Activity

You are working with Rachid who is eight years old. His teacher has asked the class to design and draw their ideal home. Rachid has screwed up his paper and says that he cannot draw as well as his friends.

1 With a partner, talk about why Rachid might say this.

2 Think of a way to help him.

Summary

Having friends is important at this age.
- Children begin to be more independent and less reliant on their families.
- Children begin to apply their knowledge and skills to new situations.
- Most children will be attending school.

Eleven to eighteen years: adolescence

Adolescence is the term used to describe the stage of growing up and maturing. Because it happens during the 'teen' years, adolescents are sometimes called teenagers. During this stage children's bodies change quickly and they become adults. This process is called **puberty**.

As well as the physical changes, teenagers are also taking on more responsibilities and becoming independent. By the age of 18, many young people are ready to start work or leave home.

Moving from being a child to being an adult

The move from childhood to adulthood can be bumpy. In this period the body produces hormones. These are chemicals that are responsible for growth and physical changes, but they are also responsible for sudden mood changes. Girls' bodies start to change earlier than boys'. The process of puberty takes about four years.

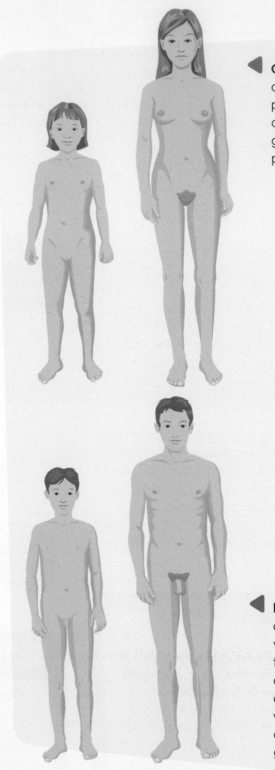

◀ **Girls** begin to develop breasts and pubic hair. By the age of 14 years, most girls have begun their periods.

◀ **Boys** develop facial and pubic hair. Their voices deepen and their sex organs develop. They grow quickly in height and weight and are, on average, taller than girls.

▲ During puberty the body's shape changes dramatically.

Learning to be an adult

As children grow, they are expected to take on more responsibilities and behave in a more grown-up way. Being an adult means having your own ideas and identity. Young people have to think about who they are and what they want to do. Parents often find that their children's behaviour keeps changing.

▲ Young people often express their identity through their clothes, hairstyles and make-up.

Gaining independence

During this period, young people start to become independent. They may start taking buses to school, going shopping with friends and later take up part-time jobs. Learning to do things away from the family is an important part of growing up.

Peer pressure

During this period, being part of a group and having friends is very important. Young people often worry about being accepted by their peers (people of the same age). Young people can find themselves under pressure to smoke, mess around at school, take drugs or have sex because they want to be liked. This is called **peer pressure**.

▲ Smoking and drug taking among young people is often the result of peer pressure. Have you ever felt under pressure to be like other people?

Pressure at school

As well as pressure to be accepted by peers, many young people are also working hard at school. At 14 years, many young people choose their exam subjects and at 16 they sit their exams. Parents and teachers put pressure on young people because qualifications are seen to be important. Some young people stop working and learning at school because of peer pressure or because they have lost some of their confidence.

Activity

1 What is meant by the word 'puberty'?
2 What is meant by the term 'peer pressure'?
3 Give an example of peer pressure.

Summary

- Adolescence is the time of growing up and maturing.
- Puberty is the physical process by which children's bodies become adult.
- During adolescence, young people learn to become more independent.
- Many teenagers feel under pressure from their peers.

Eighteen to fifty-five years: young adulthood into middle age

At 18, the law recognises young people as adults. Adulthood is the longest stage of our lives. It is marked by events and also by the ageing process.

Changes to our bodies

Pregnancy: Many women have children during this period – often between the ages of 25 and 40. Pregnancy lasts for 40 weeks and during this period the body produces high levels of hormones. The unborn baby can be harmed if the mother takes drugs, smokes or drinks lots of alcohol. Pregnant women need to eat a balanced diet.

Ageing is a gradual process of the body slowing down. Less hormones are produced and some cells are not repaired.

During this period, work and raising a family are often at the centre of people's lives.

Work: Having a job or career helps adults feel wanted and valued. Many people gain a sense of achievement from their work. Some people meet their partners at work or socialise with people from their work.

Signs of ageing

Men

Loss of hair: Some men start to lose hair during their thirties. Some will become bald.

Women

Menopause: Women usually go through the menopause or 'change' during their late forties. Their periods stop and they can no longer have children.

Both sexes

Grey hair: the first grey hairs usually begin to show when people are in their thirties.

Weight gain: Many people put on weight because their body needs less energy. Many women put weight on around their hips and bottoms. Men tend to put weight on around their stomachs.

Long sightedness: People in their forties and fifties may start to need reading glasses.

Wrinkles: The skin loses some of its firmness and elasticity.

Life events

18+
- Peak of physical health
- Start a job
- Leave home
- Find a partner

25+
- Body begins to age, but not visibly
- Set up a home
- Become a parent
- Raise children

40+
- Signs of ageing appear
- Women go through menopause
- Children leave home
- Peak of career

55+
- Noticeable slowing down of body
- Own parents may die
- Retirement
- May move closer to children
- Become a grandparent

80+
- Significant lack of stamina and strength
- May find walking difficult
- May need help in house or move to retirement home
- Become a great-grandparent

Raising a family: Having children changes people's lives. They have to put their children's needs first and be responsible for their welfare. Being a parent is not easy and some people find it hard to cope.

Social and emotional development

The way people socialise changes during their lives. Young adults often start out in groups and then split into pairs as they start relationships.

Factors affecting people's lives

Unemployment: Some people find it hard to get work or may lose their job. This can make them feel depressed as work is considered important in our society. Not having a job usually means being poor.

Separation and divorce: Not all relationships work out. Separation or divorce from partners can be bitter and cause people pain. A change in the family setting may be unsettling for children.

Case study

Graham, 37, has been made redundant from his company. He has a wife and two young children. He has been looking for work for over six months and is beginning to feel very low.

Case study

Natalie, 29, is now a single mother as her marriage has broken up. She finds it hard not having anyone around to help her with the baby. Her toddler keeps crying in the night.

18 to 25	Young adults often enjoy going out in groups. They may go to pubs, nightclubs or take part in team sports such as football. Many young people are just finding out who they are and what they want to do in life. They may meet a partner and spend more time with them than in a group.
25 to 40	Many people settle down with a partner and may get married. Couples may set up home together and start a family. They may do things with other parents such as go for a picnic or to the swimming pool or local park. This can be a time of great pressure as children are hard work and couples are often short of money.
40 to 55	Many people socialise with people who they work with. They may have hobbies and join choirs, amateur dramatic societies and fitness clubs. Many people say that they feel confident at this time in their lives because they are more mature and have survived parenthood.

Activity

Think of two people of different ages that you know.

1 What stage of life are they at?

2 What life events have they gone through?

Summary

- Visible signs of ageing include grey hair and wrinkles.
- Most women go through the menopause in their late forties.
- Key life events include settling down with a partner and raising a family.
- Social life often changes when couples have children.

Fifty-five years and over: late middle age into old age

During this period of people's lives, the ageing process continues and signs of old age become more and more obvious. Many people are frightened by the idea of becoming old, but stereotypes of middle age and old age are often untrue. Many people find this period of their lives exciting as they become free from work and from raising families. Some people begin to take up new hobbies and even return to studying!

Physical changes

The body continues to slow down and many people in late middle age find they do not have the same stamina or strength as they had in their youth. Other signs of ageing that appear in old age are often harder for people to accept and can include:

- loss of hearing
- loss of vision
- memory loss
- difficulty in walking.

Some of these signs of ageing can be reduced by good diet, exercise and being mentally active. Exercise can prevent heart disease and thinning of the bones. Hearing and sight loss are sometimes hereditary, but can be overcome through the use of aids such as hearing aids and glasses. Older people who continue to be active often live into their nineties and have a very good quality of life.

Social and emotional development

Many people find late middle age and early old age a wonderful time of life. They have learned some wisdom, are still mobile and active and are free to do as they please. Although some older people are poor, many older people have savings and personal pensions. This means that, for the first time in their lives, they can travel and take up new hobbies. Many people also enjoy having grandchildren and being with them without the tiredness and responsibility of being a parent once more!

▶ This period of life can often be very enjoyable because people have more spare time to take up new hobbies and activities.

Freedom to do what I want to do

Freedom from paying a mortgage

Freedom from raising a family

Freedom from work

Loneliness: Some people can be lonely in old age because their partner has died and their family might not live close by. It can be hard for some people to get out and their friends may have passed away.

Poor health: Some people develop heart disease and other conditions such as arthritis and diabetes. This can restrict their mobility and quality of life and they may need to take medication each day to stop the effects of the diseases. Some women also develop 'brittle bones' or osteoporosis where the bones become thin and break easily.

Factors affecting people's lives

Unemployment: People who lose their job during their late fifties do not always find another. This can mean living on benefits for the first time in their lives as they may not be able to get their pension until they are 65.

Bereavement: The death of parents and friends is common during late middle age. People of this age often lose their own parents. This can be hard as it brings home the idea that they are now the older generation in their family. Older people also find it hard because friends and family members they have known all their lives may die before them.

Activity

Lisa is in her twenties and does not want to get old. She thinks that all old people are dull and miserable.

1　Why is she wrong?

2　Think of three positive aspects of becoming old.

Case study

Mrs Jones is 59 and this year she has lost both of her parents. She feels that she has been orphaned as her parents have been around for her all her life.

Summary

● Exercise, activity and diet can reduce the effects of old age.
● Many people enjoy their retirement and old age.
● Loneliness, bereavement and poor health can affect older people.

Factors affecting growth and development

There are many factors that affect not only children's growth and development but also adults' health.

Diet

What we eat is important throughout our lives. Food provides our bodies with energy and also **nutrients** that the body needs to keep healthy. A balanced diet has all the nutrients in it that our bodies need. On page 62 we look at the types of nutrients that the body needs.

Enough, but not too many calories: The energy in food is measured in kilocalories (calories) or kilojoules. The amount of energy a body needs changes with age. As adults age they need fewer calories because they are not growing and are often using less energy. If the body is given more calories than it needs it turns them into body fat.

Age	Energy (kcal) Males	Females
10–12 months	920	865
7–10 years	1970	1740
15–18 years	2755	2110
19–50 years	2550	1940
51–59 years	2550	1900
59–64 years	2380	1900
65–74 years	2330	1900

Exercise

Exercise helps our bodies stay strong and fit. To stay healthy, everyone needs regular exercise. Children often get exercise by running around and playing outdoors. Adults may walk, jog or take part in sports to keep fit. Adults who take regular exercise live longer and stay fitter.

Exercise:
- builds muscles
- helps people to sleep
- makes people feel good
- strengthens bones
- builds stamina.

Stimulation

As well as food and physical activity, our brains also need to be stimulated (used). In young children this is important because the brain starts to build pathways (thought processes). People working with children need to look for ways to stimulate them. They may provide activities and a range of toys and equipment for children and babies to touch and explore. Talking, reading and singing to children and babies also stimulates them. If babies are not stimulated, they may have problems with learning to talk and think later on.

▲ How is the musical mobile stimulating this baby?

Adults need stimulation too!

Adults also need to keep their brains alert in order to keep their pathways open and connected. Younger people often find their work stimulates them, but people who have retired or who are at home may decide to take up a hobby in order to stay mentally fit. Look at the activities that many adults do to stimulate their brains:

- bingo
- outings
- computers
- word searches and crossword puzzles
- card games such as bridge
- board games
- reading.

Rest and sleep

As well as diet, exercise and stimulation, our bodies also need time to rest and sleep.

Factors affecting growth and development

Sleep is needed to:

- grow new cells and rest parts of the body
- help children and teenagers grow
- help the body fight off illness
- help the brain store and organise new information.

Lack of sleep makes it harder for children and adults to concentrate and learn. The amount of sleep that the body needs varies at different times in our lives.

Genetic factors

The way we grow and even the way we look is linked to our genes. Genes are messages that tell the cells in our body how to grow and develop. Certain genes are responsible for the colour of your eyes, your height and your skin colour. Everyone except identical twins or triplets has their own mixture of genes or 'genetic makeup'. This is why everyone looks slightly different. Identical twins have the same 'genetic makeup' because they came from the same egg. Our genes come from our parents and this is why families tend to share certain looks. Genes can also affect our health and development. Conditions such as cystic fibrosis and haemophilia are linked to genes.

Wealth

The amount of money people have can affect their health and development. For example, people who are well off tend to live for longer because they can afford better housing and food.

Activity

Janus is five years old. He is scared that there are monsters under his bed. He is not getting very much sleep at night because he is too afraid.

1 With a partner, think of different signs that might show that Janus is not getting much sleep.

2 Can you think of any ways to help him feel less afraid?

Summary

- Diet can affect children's growth and development and adults' health.
- The genes we inherit from our parents affect the way we grow and some aspects of our development.
- Sleep, exercise and stimulation are needed by adults and children to stay healthy.

Language and communication skills

On pages 26–27 we looked at the principles of communicating with children. Communication is more than just talking and listening; it also covers reading and writing, signing and showing our feelings through body language.

▲ Does your mind wander to other things during a conversation? Why might this affect the quality of the conversation?

Why is communication so important?

Language and communication are used to:
- build relationships with friends, families and people we meet
- express our feelings and needs
- give out and receive information.

Language is also connected to thought processes. It is an important tool for our memories. A single word or phrase can bring back memories. Many people also need language to help them organise their thoughts.

Factors affecting language and communication

There are many factors that can affect people's language and communication. These can make it harder for them to get their needs met or to build relationships. Children who have difficulties in communicating often become frustrated because they cannot make others understand what they want.

Hearing loss

If someone cannot hear very well, they may not always understand what is happening and may not be able to join in a conversation. Other people may become impatient with them and they may feel lonely. To help them communicate, people with severe hearing loss may use:
- hearing aids
- lip reading
- sign language
- written messages.

Hearing loss in children
Some children are born with a hearing impairment. This is often diagnosed during a child's first year of life. They may be given hearing aids to help them hear more. Some children who are unable to hear learn to communicate by using sign language. Many other children also have temporary hearing loss which is caused by the build-up of fluid in their ears. This is sometimes called glue ear and children may have an operation to put a grommet or drain into their ears.

Hearing loss can prevent children from learning to speak and also from learning to read. Some signs of hearing loss in children over the age of three years include:
- speech is difficult to understand or muffled (children over four years)
- intently watching people's faces and lips
- lips moving silently when listening
- not turning head or responding when name is called
- lacking interest in stories or in watching television
- frustration or aggressive behaviour.

Hearing loss in older people
As part of the ageing process, people lose the ability to hear some sounds.

Visual impairment or sight loss

People who cannot see can find it harder to communicate, read and write. They may use these aids to help them:

- books with large print
- braille
- CDs.

Sight loss in children

It is rare for children to be born unable to see, although many children need to wear glasses. Signs to look for include:

- squinting or peering
- difficulties in learning to read
- lack of interest in watching television
- clumsiness – e.g. walking over toys or bumping into things.

Sight loss in older people

As part of the aging process, the muscles in the eyes start to work less well. This causes long sightedness. Many older people need glasses to read. Older people may also lose their sight if they have eye conditions like cataracts or glaucoma. Accidents can also cause sight loss.

Language barriers

Not all children and adults in the UK speak English. This can be a barrier to communication, and body language and signs may be used to help communication. Young children can quickly learn English if they are given plenty of help and are made to feel valued. Sometimes a translator may be needed to pass on and receive information.

Medical conditions

Some children and adults have medical conditions that affect their language and communication. Some children have learning difficulties or a medical condition which prevents them from speaking. They may use Makaton (a simple sign language) or a board with signs to communicate.

In older people, illnesses such as strokes and dementia, as well as accidents, can damage the brain and cause speech and memory loss. Speech therapy can sometimes help the person to learn how to speak again.

Activity

Look at this conversation. How is language being used?

Shaheen: What time are you going out?

Sanjay: I think Darren said that he'd pick me up at half past four.

Shaheen: Could you do me a favour, love, and get me some stamps while you're out?

Sanjay: Yes, OK. Is there anything else you need?

Shaheen: No. Just a hug and a cup of tea if you're making one.

Summary

- Language and communication help people build relationships and gain information.
- Adults working with children need to look out for signs of hearing and visual impairment.
- As part of the ageing process, many older people will need glasses and may lose some hearing.

Emotional and social needs

Keeping healthy is not only about looking after the body, but also the mind. The way children and adults feel can affect their health and development. Children and adults who are feeling secure and content tend to be healthier, so 'mental health' is important.

Self-esteem

Self-esteem is about the way we think of ourselves. People who have high self-esteem will be more confident because they feel good about themselves. Self-esteem is important as it affects people's feelings of happiness and well-being. It is a major factor in people's mental health. When people have very low self-esteem, they do not always take care of themselves. They may see themselves as being second best. Low self-esteem can often lead to drug taking, not eating properly, violent relationships and even suicide.

For some adults, low self-esteem may have begun in childhood due to being bullied, abused or feeling unloved. The diagram above shows a number of other reasons why people may have low self-esteem.

- Being discriminated against
- Living on benefits or in poverty
- Losing a job
- Separation or divorce from a partner
- Falling out with family and friends
- **Reasons why people may have low self-esteem**
- Not having a partner or not being in a stable relationship
- Loneliness
- Disability or coping with an illness
- Not coping or being bullied at work
- Disliking their appearance

Self-esteem and children: People working with children need to make them feel good about themselves. Children who have high self-esteem find it easier to learn and also to make friends. Children gain their confidence mainly through adults; especially their own families.

- Do not compare children or have favourites.
- Do not tease children.
- Make sure you do not talk negatively about children.
- Smile and greet children.
- **Tips for keeping children's self-esteem high**
- Praise children as much as possible.
- Make sure you step in if children make unkind comments to each other.
- Be careful about commenting on children's appearance.
- Always report any signs of bullying to your supervisor.

> My dad walked out and my mum's always criticising me. I'm better off here on the streets. At least my dog loves me.

Thanks

▲ Why does this teenager have low self-esteem? What could other people do to help him?

Love and approval

Adults as well as children need to feel wanted, liked and respected. It is a basic need and helps people's self-esteem. People seek love and approval from their family and friends. Adults may also gain approval from work colleagues, while school children may gain approval from their teachers and peers. Retired people can sometimes lose self-esteem because they are no longer gaining approval from work colleagues.

Babies and children learn that they are loved and wanted by looking closely at adults' faces. This means that it is important for babies and young children to get smiles and cuddles from the people in their families.

Relationships

Most people are sociable and enjoy being with others. Adults and children have a range of relationships such as with family, friends, peers and partners. Having good relationships with the people around us can help our self-esteem and is an important need. This is why falling out with friends or separating from a partner can make people lose their confidence. It is also why being single can be hard, especially for older people, who may not be able to get out of their homes.

Learning social skills

Good relationships depend on people using their social skills. Children need to learn these social skills. At first they cannot share and expect others to do everything they want but, by the age of four years, most children have started to play with other children.

Security

Most children and adults need to feel secure. They need to know that their friends and family will be there for them. Most people also have routines in their lives. Babies and young children need routines so they can predict what will happen next. They need to know that the same people will be looking after them and that the day will have a familiar pattern.

Adults also need financial security, which means having enough money to live on. When people lose their jobs, they lose their financial security.

Activity

Complete the sentences.

1 The way we think of ourselves is known as S _ _ _- E _ _ _ _ _.

2 People may have low self-esteem because of D _ _ _ _ _ E, L _ _ _ _ _ _ _ _ S and P _ _ _ _ _ Y among other things.

3 S _ _ _ _ _ _ Y is very important for babies and children.

Summary

- People's self-esteem can affect their well-being.
- Children need adults to help build their self-esteem.
- Adults and children need love, approval and security.

Patience – e.g. waiting for turns

Social skills that children learn gradually

Courtesy and manners – e.g. saying 'please' and 'thank you'

Communication skills – e.g. being able to listen as well as talk

Empathy – e.g. seeing things from other people's points of view

End of unit summary

One way of finding out more about people is by asking them to fill in a questionnaire. Look at the questionnaire below, which has been designed to ask teenagers about themselves.

Getting ready for assessment

For this unit you need to produce a portfolio that shows that you understand the development of babies through to adults. You need to produce information about five different ages:

- one baby
- one child
- one teenager
- one middle-aged adult
- one elderly person.

Top tips for designing questionnaires

- Think about the information you need to collect.
- Do not make the questionnaire too long.
- Write some open questions.
- Make sure the questionnaire is suitable for different groups of people.
- Make sure the questionnaire is neat and the spelling is correct.
- Get someone to look at your questionnaire before trying it out.

It is important to tell people why you are asking them questions.

It is polite to thank them for helping you.

Tell people what they have to do in each section of the questionnaire.

Some people do not want to write down their exact age. They prefer to circle an age band.

As part of my college course, I am doing some research about human growth and development. I am collecting information to see what people do at different stages of their lives.

I would be grateful if you could spend a few minutes filling in this questionnaire. Thank you for your help.

(Please circle)
I am   13–15 years
            16–19 years

(Please circle)
I am   at school   in college
            at work   in training

Skills
What skills do you have to use?

_____

_____

Hobbies and social life
What do you do in your free time?

_____

_____

Interests and lifestyle
(Please circle)
Do you have any health problems?

Yes   No

(Please circle)
Do you think that you have a healthy life style?   Yes   No

Please state why

_____

_____

Relationship
(Please circle)
I live   with my parent(s)
              with my partner
              by myself
              with my child(ren)

Future
What are your future plans?

_____

_____

Is there anything that you would like to change about your life?

_____

_____

What things do you enjoy about your life?

_____

_____

Thank you for taking the time to fill in this questionnaire.

Phrases such as 'please state why' encourage people to give you extra information.

Questions such as 'what are your future plans?' are open questions. Open questions give you more information than questions that allow people just to write 'yes' or 'no'.

End of unit task 1: Questionnaires

In pairs, design different questionnaires that would give you information about these groups of people:

- a baby (a parent could fill it in)
- a child (a parent or an older child could fill it in)
- a teenager
- a middle-aged adult
- an elderly person.

Once you have found out more information, you will need to think about what each person has said and how it links to what you have read about in this book and what you have been taught. With your tutor, you will also need to think about how you will present the information.

End of unit task 2: Healthy advice

Look at the letter below from Anna.

> Dear Agony Aunt,
>
> I am 18 years old and have just lost my job. I am really fed up and am finding it hard to sleep at night. I am also quite lonely as I have just moved and don't know anyone of my age. I am also finding it hard to eat properly as I cannot be bothered to cook anything. I spend most evenings alone watching television. Help!

- Can you give Anna some advice as to what she should do?
- How might this situation damage Anna's overall health?

Back to the real world

You have now found out about how children develop throughout their lives. You have also seen the factors that are important in keeping babies, children and adults happy and healthy.

1 Can you pick out a milestone for each of these groups of children: 0–1, 1–3, 3–5 and 5–11 years?
2 Can you list three factors that affect people's overall health?
3 Can you explain why stimulation is important throughout life?

Glossary

attachment The process by which babies learn to love their main carers; usually parents

bonding The process by which babies learn to love their main carers; usually parents

cognitive development The process of learning how to organise information and thoughts

peer pressure Feeling as if you should do things to be like others of the same age

puberty The period in which children's bodies change to become adults

reflexes Actions or movements that are not controlled

Unit 3 Food and nutrition

Most childcare settings serve food and drinks to children. Consuming food and water is a basic need for everyone. Adults working with children need to understand how to give them a balanced and healthy diet. They also need to understand how to encourage children to eat food and how to cook and serve it.

This unit will help you to choose food that will help children of different ages grow and develop and also to prepare and serve food safely. This unit also explains how to meet the needs of children who have special food requirements.

The unit covers the following:

- what constitutes a balanced diet
- how to prepare and present food for children
- the principles of feeding babies
- different food requirements for religious, cultural and other reasons.

The topics you will find in this unit are:

- A balanced diet
- Food for children of different ages
- Preparing food safely and hygienically
- Preventing food poisoning
- Presenting food and making mealtimes social occasions
- Feeding babies
- Preparing feeds and sterilising feeding equipment
- Weaning
- Food for babies
- Food requirements
- Food allergies and medical conditions

In the real world

You are on placement. Your supervisor asks you to help prepare the snacks for the children and to help at lunchtime. You are not sure quite what to do.

By the end of this unit, you will know about the types of food that should be given to children and how to prepare food hygienically. You will also know how to help babies when it is time for weaning.

A balanced diet

Everyone needs food and water to live. Food and water help our bodies to stay healthy. Giving babies and children the right amount and types of food will give them the energy they need to grow. This is what is meant by a **balanced diet**.

What's in food?

To find out about balanced diets, we need to know what is in food and why the body needs it. All food contains **nutrients**. There are five different types of nutrients:

- carbohydrates
- proteins
- fats
- vitamins
- minerals.

We need to eat a range of foods so that our bodies can get all of these nutrients. Our bodies also need water. Plain water does not contain any nutrients but the body cannot live without it. Drinks that we give children, like milk and juice, contain water.

How the body uses the nutrients

The table on page 63 shows the types of food in which nutrients are found. It also shows how the body uses these nutrients.

Choosing foods that are nutritious

Foods or meals that have several nutrients in them are called 'nutritious'. Babies and children need meals that are nutritious to stay healthy and help them grow. You can read labels on foods to find out about the nutrients that are in them. Nutritious meals are usually made up of several foods.

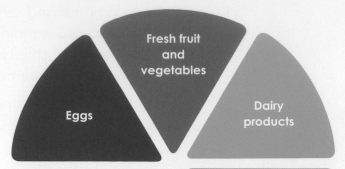

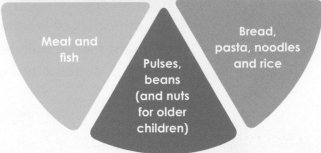

▲ Most balanced diets have foods from several of these groups.

▲ A balanced diet keeps children healthy, but eating food can also be fun!

Nutrient	Why the body needs it	Examples of foods where it can be found
Carbohydrate	For energy	Foods made with flour – bread, pasta, noodles, potatoes, yams, bananas, plantains, sweet potatoes, rice, beans and pulses
Fat	For energy	Butter, margarine, vegetable oils. Fat is also in meats, fish and many dairy products.
Protein	Helps the body to grow and repair cells	Meat, eggs, fish, milk and dairy products. Protein is also found when combinations of foods such as peas, beans, wheat and corn are eaten together.
Vitamins	There are many different vitamins which help the body in several ways.	
Vitamin A	For eyes and eyesight	Carrots, milk, apricots, fatty fish, margarine and butter
Vitamin B (There are several in this group.)	Good for the nervous system. Helps to release energy from other foods	Bread, meat, yeast, pasta, flour, rice and noodles
Vitamin C	Good for skin and gums	Fresh fruit and vegetables, especially oranges, kiwis, blackcurrants, green peppers
Vitamin D	Good for teeth and bones	Milk, margarine, cheese, yoghurts
Vitamin E	Not completely understood	Green leafy vegetables, milk, wheatgerm, vegetable oil
Minerals	The body needs many different minerals. You need to know about these two.	
Iron	Helps the blood to carry oxygen	Red meat, broccoli, spinach, plain chocolate, egg yolk
Calcium	Good for teeth and bones	Milk, cheese, yoghurts and other dairy products

Activity

Children need meals that have plenty of nutrients in them.

Which of these meals do you think has the most nutrients?

1 Sandwiches with tuna, green peppers and cheese; milk

2 Sausages and mash; water

3 Spaghetti with cheese and butter; a fizzy drink

Summary

- Water has no nutrients in it but is essential for the body.
- The body needs food for energy, growth and to stay healthy.
- Food contains nutrients.
- There are five different types of nutrients that the body needs.
- A balanced diet means having enough of each type of nutrient.

Food for children of different ages

Everyone needs a balanced diet that has the five nutrients in it (see page 62–63). Children also need more energy as they get older to help their bodies grow. As children grow, so the amount of energy (or calories) they need increases. This means that as children get older they need to eat more food and will need larger helpings. To make sure young children get enough nutrients and energy, adults have to plan their diet carefully. Foods such as sweets and chips should not be given often as they do not contain a range of nutrients.

▲ What might this child learn by making her own lunch?

Age	Energy (kcal)	
	Boys	Girls
1–3 years	1230	1165
4–6 years	1715	1545
7–10 years	1970	1740
11–14 years	2220	1845
15–18 years	2755	2110
Adults	2550	1940

Following children's appetites

It is always best to follow children's appetites. A child who asks for more food or who says they are hungry may well be going through a **growth spurt**. A child who normally eats well but does not feel hungry may be feeling ill. If you are worried about how much a child is eating, you should talk to your supervisor.

Making sure meals are suitable for children

Young children find it hard to chew and to use cutlery to cut up their food. This means that meals need to be easy for them to eat. Older children often enjoy serving and cooking meals for themselves.

Introducing new foods

It is a good idea for young children to get used to a wide range of tastes. This will ensure their diet is balanced and also make it easier for them to try out new foods later on. Children often notice what adults are eating. Older children may start to 'pick' at their food if they see adults not eating theirs. It also means they may try a new food out if they see an adult enjoying it.

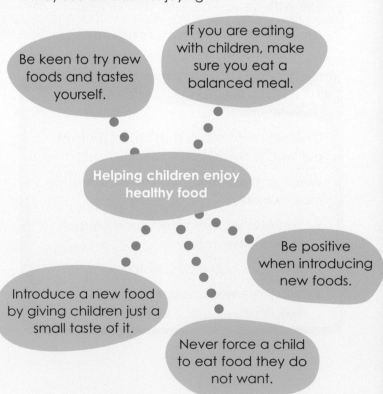

Be keen to try new foods and tastes yourself.

If you are eating with children, make sure you eat a balanced meal.

Helping children enjoy healthy food

Be positive when introducing new foods.

Introduce a new food by giving children just a small taste of it.

Never force a child to eat food they do not want.

Changing tastes

Most people have food likes and dislikes. Children are no different, but their tastes often change. Children often begin to like foods that they would not eat before. This means that it can be a good idea to encourage a child to try the food again later – perhaps cooked or served in a different way.

Snacks and drinks

It is not wrong to give children snacks as long as they are **nutritious** and will not spoil their appetite for a main meal. Toddlers and young children have small stomachs. This means that they may feel hungry between meals and will need some small snacks to keep them going. Children who are growing rapidly may also feel hungry between meals. Giving children sweets and crisps fills them up, but does not give them enough nutrients.

▲ Children need to be offered snacks that are nutritious.

Drinks

Children need to be offered drinks throughout the day. The best drinks are water and milk. The body needs water for many reasons, such as keeping cool during hot weather and helping digest food. Milk is a good drink for children because it is full of nutrients and also gives children energy. Drinks that are sugary can spoil children's appetites and also their teeth. Drinks that taste sugary also encourage a sweet tooth. Fruit juices naturally contain sugar and so should be diluted with water to prevent tooth decay.

Summary

- Children need more energy as they get older.
- Children's tastes can change.
- Young children need food that is easy to eat.
- Children may need nutritious snacks between meals.
- Milk and water are the best drinks for children.

Preparing food safely and hygienically

Many accidents happen in kitchens. This is why there should be a first aid kit in the kitchen. Children should be kept out of the kitchen, and safety equipment such as cooker guards should be used.

Safety in the kitchen

There are many dangers in the kitchen. Knives and other tools can easily cut children. Kettles, irons and saucepans can burn or scald children badly. Many kitchens also have cleaning products in them. Children can be poisoned by them. This is why many childcare settings have safety gates to prevent children from coming into kitchens.

The diagram below shows safety points to consider when using a microwave.

Food poisoning

Food poisoning can sometimes kill babies and young children. To prevent food poisoning, you need to know how to prepare and store food safely.

What causes food poisoning?

Food poisoning is caused by large numbers of bacteria on food that enter our bodies when we swallow the food. Signs of food poisoning include sickness, diarrhoea and flu-like symptoms. Bacteria can be spread to food by flies, dirty hands and during the preparation process. Bacteria that are already on food can grow quickly if the food is left out rather than being refrigerated.

On the pages 68–69 you will be able to read about steps you can take to prevent food poisoning.

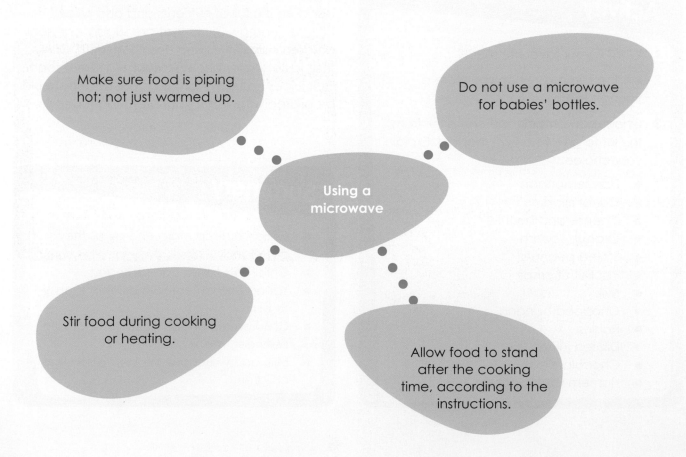

Make sure food is piping hot; not just warmed up.

Do not use a microwave for babies' bottles.

Using a microwave

Stir food during cooking or heating.

Allow food to stand after the cooking time, according to the instructions.

▲ Does this look like a safe and hygienic kitchen yo you?

Activity

Look at the kitchen in the illustration.

1 How many dangers can you spot?

2 How can these dangers be prevented?

Summary

- Children should be kept out of kitchens wherever possible.
- Supervise children carefully if they are in the kitchen.
- Keep knives and other tools away from young children.
- Lock cleaning products away from children.

◀ Would you feel like eating this if you knew her hands were dirty?

Preventing food poisoning

There are four steps we can take to prevent food poisoning.

1 Buy, store and use foods safely

The food we buy or use needs to be fresh and in date. This means it is more likely to be safe. Once bought, frozen or refrigerated foods should not be left out for long periods.

- Check how long food can be kept once opened.
- Check the use-by date.
- Make sure food is stored properly, for example dry foods need to be kept in sealed containers in a dry place.
- Never take a risk – do not use a suspect food.

2 Prevent bacteria from spreading onto food

Wherever possible, try to stop bacteria from reaching food or from being spread from food to food.

- Tie long hair back.
- Wear an apron.
- Scrub your hands before touching food.
- Wash your hands after touching raw food.
- Keep your hands clean during food preparation.
- Cover any cuts with plasters (blue ones are often used by food handlers).
- Keep raw food covered and away from cooked food.

- Use separate chopping boards, spoons, bowls, etc., for raw and cooked food.
- Cover food up or put it in sealed containers so that flies cannot lay eggs on it.
- Keep lids on waste bins and empty them often.
- Clean surfaces in the kitchen: tops, floors, sink.
- Do not lick spoons and put them back in food!
- Keep animals out of the kitchen.

3 Slow bacteria down

Some foods have bacteria on them. Small amounts of bacteria are harmless but, if left to grow, bacteria can make us ill. Bacteria grow very fast. They love warmth and water. As most foods have water in them, all that bacteria need to start multiplying is warmth.

- Keep food in the refrigerator. This slows the growth down, but does not stop it.
- Check that the fridge is at the correct temperature.
- Follow the instructions when defrosting frozen foods.
- Throw away food if it has been left out.
- Do not refreeze food once it has been thawed. Freezing does not kill bacteria.
- Throw away food if it is past its use-by date.

4 Kill off bacteria

Bacteria can be killed if they are heated to a temperature of 70°C for several minutes. Food that is only warmed through can be dangerous because the bacteria will have had a chance to grow but not be killed off. Food that is left warming can therefore be dangerous.

- Boil drinking water for babies and allow it to cool.
- Always follow recipes or instruction carefully.
- Do not leave food to warm.
- If heating food for babies and children, make sure it is piping hot and then allow it to cool down.
- Never keep reheated food – once cooked, it can only be reheated once.

Activity

Make a poster that will help an early years worker remember how to prevent food poisoning.

Summary

- Food poisoning can kill.
- Food poisoning is caused by large numbers of bacteria on food.
- Bacteria can be killed by heating food to a high temperature.
- Food must be stored carefully.
- Adults preparing food need to wash their hands.

Presenting food and making mealtimes social occasions

Mealtimes are important moments in the day. They are times for people to come together, talk and enjoy their food. Adults have an important role in presenting food and making mealtimes fun.

Presenting food

Children are more likely to eat and enjoy their food if it looks good. It also has to be easy for them to eat as young children find it hard to cut up their food. When serving food, you should always check whether any children have special diets or needs when eating (see also pages 80–83).

Making mealtimes social occasions

Children will eat more if they are relaxed and are enjoying being with others. You should try to sit with children when they are eating and encourage them to talk. Young children often need plenty of time to eat and forcing them to eat quickly does not work. Toddlers are very messy and you will need to have some things to hand to clean them up! Mealtimes are also a chance for children to practise and learn some social skills. You can encourage them to pass food to each other and to have a go at serving themselves.

- Encourage children to serve themselves food and pour drinks.
- Children learn by copying so say 'please' and 'thank you'.
- Talk to the children as they are eating.
- Sing songs and rhymes with children when they have finished but are waiting for pudding or for others to finish.
- Do not force children to eat food – they may be feeling ill.
- Allow children to eat at their own speed.

▲ What skills will these children learn at mealtimes?

Make faces out of food on the plate.

Give food special names – e.g. 'pirate potatoes' or 'brilliant beans'.

Have some parties – e.g. a red day with foods that have red or pink in them.

Do not put more on a plate than a child can manage.

Tips for making food appealing

Make sure there is some colour on the plate – e.g. carrots, peppers.

Avoid food that needs a lot of chewing or cutting up.

Put food onto decorative plates.

Mealtime safety

Hygiene
- Wash your hands before serving food.
- Make sure children have washed their hands before eating.
- Do not use the same spoon to feed different toddlers or children.
- Make sure children do not share beakers, cups or cutlery.
- Use separate cloths, tissues or flannels to wipe each child's face and hands.
- Throw away any unfinished foods that have been started (the bacteria from the child's mouth will have been transferred onto the food and will start to grow).

Scalds and burns
- Do not leave hot drinks within children's reach.
- Always check that food and plates are not too hot.
- Stir foods and drinks that have been heated using a microwave to make sure they are evenly heated.
- Remember that food that has been microwaved continues cooking. Follow the manufacturers' instructions and allow foods to stand before serving.

Choking
- Toddlers and young children can easily choke on foods.
- Never leave children unsupervised at mealtimes.
- Do not give peanuts or grapes to toddlers as they can choke on them.

High chairs
- High chairs help babies and toddlers to join in at mealtimes.
- Always strap babies and toddlers in so they do not fall out.
- Make sure you can get them out quickly in case they begin to choke.
- Make sure high chairs are not placed where other children might be able to knock them over.

Activity

Tania is four years old and her mum says she is a fussy eater. On today's menu there are Brussels sprouts. Tania has not had these before.

1 How might you encourage Tania to try them?

2 Compare your ideas with the other members of your class.

Summary

- Mealtimes should be relaxed and enjoyable.
- Children can learn social skills during mealtimes.
- All children need to be supervised while eating.
- Everyone should wash their hands before eating or touching food.

Feeding babies

Up until the age of around six months, babies are fed only on milk. The milk babies are given will provide them with the nutrients and energy they need for their first few months.

Types of milk

Babies can be breast fed or bottle fed. There are advantages to both types of feeding, although breast feeding is thought to be better for the baby.

Breast feeding: Breast milk is very good for babies as it contains **antibodies** from the mother which help the baby fight off illnesses. It is also easier for babies to digest than bottle milk. Many mothers prefer breast feeding because they enjoy being close to their babies and do not need to sterilise bottles. It is possible for breast milk to be **expressed** and fed to the baby later by someone else, but the bottle needs to be sterilised. Breast-feeding mothers need plenty to drink and must eat well.

Bottle feeding: Most bottles for babies are made up using specially designed powdered milk known as formula milk, although it is possible to buy ready made-up formula milk. There are different types of formula milk for babies to suit babies' needs and for babies of different ages. Some mothers prefer bottle feeding because their partner can take turns to feed the baby.

- Sterilise bottles to avoid food poisoning.
- Follow instructions carefully when making up bottles.
- Use the correct type of formula milk.

Feeding a baby

Feeding is a very special time for a baby. It helps the baby to feel loved and secure and stops them feeling hungry. Never leave babies to feed themselves, even if they can hold the bottle. They may choke and they are also missing out on a special moment.

How much milk?

Babies should be fed 'on demand' and given as much milk as they want. They should not be forced to finish off a bottle. Any leftover milk should be thrown away. Always note down the time and the amount of milk a baby has had.

▲ Feeding is an important moment for a baby. Look how this baby gazes into the eyes of his mother.

How to feed a baby

1  Wash your hands.

2  Make sure you find a quiet and comfortable place to feed the baby.

3  Have everything you need to hand – e.g. bottle, tissues and bib.

4 Check the temperature of the milk by testing it on your wrist.

5  Put the baby on your lap and let their head rest against your arm.

6  Gently touch the baby's lips with the teat. Never force the teat into the baby's mouth.

7 Make sure the bottle is held at a right angle so that the milk is covering the teat.

8  Allow the baby to have a break and feed at their own pace.

Feeding problems

- Some babies are sick after their feed. A little bit of sick is usually caused by some wind but, if babies are very sick, get help straight away.
- Some babies also get colic. They scream and are in pain. If a baby is crying, you should stay calm and get help.
- If a baby has not taken much milk or does not seem hungry, you should talk to your placement supervisor or the parents. It may be that the baby is feeling ill.

Activity

With a partner, talk about what you should do in the following situations.

1 You have been asked to feed a baby. What three things should you do before giving her the bottle?

2 A baby you are feeding does not seem hungry. What should you do?

Summary

- Babies can be breast fed or bottle fed.
- Formula milk is used to make up most bottles.
- Feeding helps babies feel loved and secure.
- Never leave a baby to feed itself.

Preparing feeds and sterilising feeding equipment

Preparing feeds and sterilising feeding equipment is an important part of working with babies. Babies rely on adults to feed them and keep them safe.

Preparing a feed

Preparing a feed is a big responsibility. The amount of powder has to be accurate and depends on a baby's weight; not their age. You must check how much a baby weighs and then read carefully how many scoops of powder are needed. Feeds also need preparing before a baby is hungry so that the baby is not kept waiting.

Making up and storing feeds

It is possible to make up several feeds at once. Once made up they should be cooled down quickly (the bottles can be put into cold water) and then kept in the fridge. Bottles must be used within 24 hours. To heat bottles that have already been made up, simply stand them in a jug or bowl of hot water.

- Do *not* microwave bottles as the babies can be scalded by the uneven heating of the milk.
- *Throw away* any milk that is left after a feed.

Making up a feed

1 Check which type of milk you should use. Read the instructions carefully.

2 Fill a kettle and let it boil. Allow the water to cool down.

3 Wash your hands carefully.

4 Using a sterilised bottle, put in the boiled water to the level needed.

5 Using a scoop, measure the amount of powdered milk needed for the weight of the baby. Level off the scoop with a knife.

6 Add the powder to the sterilised bottle.

7 Screw the ring and disc on the bottle, but not the teat.

8 Shake the bottle well.

9 Allow the bottle to cool down and then put the teat on the bottle.

10 Check the temperature before giving the baby the bottle.

Sterilising feeding equipment

Sterilising feeding equipment helps kill off bacteria which can cause food poisoning.

How to sterilise equipment

There are four main ways of sterilising. It is important to find out how your setting sterilises equipment. Ask someone to show you. Before sterilising any equipment, you should make sure that it has been washed.

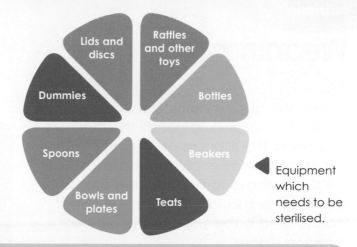

Equipment which needs to be sterilised.

	How the sterilising method works	Safety points
Sterilising tablets	• Sterilising tablets or liquid are added to cold water. • Equipment is put under the water for 30 minutes. • Everything is then rinsed in boiled water to remove the chemicals.	• Make sure you know how many tablets or how much liquid you should be putting into the water. • Equipment must not float on top of the water, but must be pushed underneath. • Everything has to be properly rinsed with water that has been boiled and then allowed to cool.
Steam steriliser	• This piece of equipment sterilises bottles by the use of steam. • Equipment that has been washed is put upside down in the unit. • The lid is placed on the unit and the unit is switched on.	• Read the manufacturer's instructions before using. • Make sure items are already washed and clean. • Items should not touch each other. • Do not open the unit until it has finished working and has cooled.
Boiling	• Equipment is placed in a saucepan with water. • Water is boiled for at least ten minutes.	• Make sure that only items that can be boiled are put in. • Do not allow the pan to boil dry. • Allow the pan to cool before taking items out.
Microwave steriliser	• This piece of equipment is used to go inside microwave ovens. • Equipment that has been washed is put upside down in the unit. • The microwave is switched on.	• Do not put any metal items such as spoons inside the unit. • Follow the manufacturer's instructions carefully. • Leave to cool before taking things out.

Activity

Are the following statements true or false?

1 The amount of milk powder depends on a baby's weight.
2 Bottles can be heated in a microwave.
3 Feeding equipment should be sterilised until babies are at least six months old.

Summary

• Making up feeds is a big responsibility.
• Always c heck the weight of the baby and the type of milk they have.
• Always sterilise feeding equipment to prevent food poisoning.

Weaning

By the age of six months, babies need more than just milk to get all the nutrients they need. The process of helping them eat ordinary food is called weaning. There are three stages to the weaning process. You need to know these as well as what food to feed babies during the different weaning stages.

Why weaning is important

After six months, milk alone will not give babies enough energy, iron and vitamins. Adding food to babies' diets gives them more energy and nutrients, although babies and young children still need milk in their diets. Babies who are not weaned may lose weight and not have enough energy. Chewing food also helps babies to develop muscles in their mouths which will help them to talk.

Signs that babies need weaning

There are signs that babies need weaning and most babies begin weaning at six months. Weaning babies before six months is not a good idea because their stomachs are not ready to take food. Some babies may also develop allergies if they are weaned too early.

Signs that a baby needs weaning include that the baby:

● is hungrier
● begins to wake more often in the night to be fed
● begins to put on less weight.

▲ Self-feeding can be a messy experience at first, but one the baby will find enjoyable.

Starting the weaning process

Babies have to learn to take food from a spoon and to get used to the feel of it in their mouths. This means that the first foods used in weaning are not thick and do not need chewing. Most babies start by having a teaspoonful of baby rice mixed with milk during one of their normal feeds. Many babies spit out their first spoonfuls so it is important that you wear an apron and that the baby wears a bib!

Remember
- Spoons, plates and bowls must be sterilised.
- Do not get cross with the baby if they are not interested. Try again another day.

Activity

Can you give some advice to this parent?

Dear Kate,

My baby son is six months old. He has started to cry quite a lot in the day and seems to suck his hand. He used to sleep in the night, but now wakes up. I thought he was hungry and so I gave him some baby rice, but he spat it out. I am not sure whether I should try it again or leave it for another month or so. What do you think?

Jennie

P.S. My friend says that there is no need to sterilise feeding equipment now. Is this true?

Summary

- Most babies are weaned at six months.
- Babies' plates, spoons and bowls must be sterilised.
- It can take a while for babies to get used to eating.

Food for babies

Babies need to try out a range of foods. This will help them later to enjoy a balanced diet. Babies need to get used to many different flavours.

Starting weaning

To start the process of weaning, babies are often only offered one food at a time. This is to check that they are not allergic to foods. Once a baby seems fine on a food, it can be mixed with others that the baby has already tried – for example, puréed apple and banana mixed together. Many babies are given baby rice to start off with.

Preparing foods for babies

It is important not to add any salt or sugar to babies' foods. Salt can cause kidney problems and sugar can damage teeth – even those still up in the gums. It is possible to buy baby food, but it is cheaper and easy to make your own. Remember that equipment used in feeding babies needs to be sterilised.

How much food should babies be given?

The best guides are the babies themselves. Most babies turn their heads away when they have had enough food. They may then be ready for their milk or another drink. Once babies start weaning, they often need more to drink. Beakers with spouts can be used to help them learn to drink out of cups. The best drink for babies is water that has been boiled and then allowed to cool. If a baby does not seem hungry and has not had any food, you should always tell your placement supervisor or the parents. Never force a baby to eat – they may choke.

▲ It is important that weaning is enjoyable for babies.

Age	Stage	Types of food	Comments
6 months	Puréed foods	• Fruit • Vegetables • Baby rice mixed with milk	• Equipment must be sterilised. • Babies may take food slowly. • Babies must be offered cold water that has been boiled as they may become thirsty.
9 months	Mashed or minced foods	• Fruit • Vegetables • Meat and fish • Cereals, rice and beans • Family meals, with no salt or sugar, that have been mashed up	• Supervise babies carefully in case they choke. • Make sure they are harnessed if in high chairs. • Offer babies drinks.
12 months	Mashed and finger foods	• Meals that have been mashed up • Foods that the baby can pick up and eat alone – e.g. strips of bread, banana, fish fingers • Salty and sugary foods must not be given.	• Supervise babies carefully in case they choke. • Make sure they are harnessed if in high chairs. • Offer babies drinks.

Foods that must be avoided

There are some foods that babies must not be given:

- **salt**: salty foods such as crisps. Salt should not be added to food either.
- **liver**
- **uncooked eggs**: eggs have to be cooked all the way through.
- **nuts**: some children are allergic to nuts. Nuts can also make babies choke.
- **sugary foods**: babies do not need sugar or sweets.

Activity

There are two mistakes in this menu for a six-month-old baby. What are they and why?

- Soft-boiled egg
- Toast strips with peanut butter
- Puréed apple
- Cool boiled water

Summary

- Babies need to be weaned so they get enough nutrients.
- Most babies are weaned at six months.
- Feeding equipment must be sterilised.
- By 12 months, most babies can feed themselves using their fingers.

Food requirements

Some adults and children have special food requirements. They may have allergies, be vegetarian or may not eat certain foods because of religious beliefs. You need to know the different food requirements of the children you are working with so that you can make sure they are not given food they are not supposed to eat.

Food requirements for religious reasons

Some families belong to religious groups and, as part of their religion, they may have particular food requirements. This may mean that they do not eat some foods or that foods need to be prepared in a certain way. Jews and Muslims, for example, will only eat meat if the animal has been killed in a certain way. This is what is meant by kosher and halal.

Below is a chart that shows some of the main food requirements of different religious groups, but you will also need to find out more from your supervisor or a child's parents.

> Always check before giving children any food or drink – even a sweet.

Religious groups	Comments
Hindus	<ul><li>Mainly vegetarian.</li><li>Hindus do not eat beef.</li><li>Dairy products that do not contain rennet.</li><li>Pork is not usually eaten.</li></ul>
Sikhs	<ul><li>Some Sikhs are vegetarian; others will eat lamb, chicken and fish.</li><li>Pork is not usually eaten.</li><li>Sikhs do not eat beef.</li></ul>
Jews	<ul><li>Meat must be **kosher**.</li><li>Jews do not eat pork, shellfish or fish without fins and scales.</li><li>Separate cooking dishes must be used for dairy products.</li><li>Dairy products and meat are not eaten together.</li></ul>
Muslims	<ul><li>Meat must be **halal**.</li><li>Muslims do not eat pork and some do not eat cheese.</li><li>Dairy products that do not contain rennet.</li><li>During **Ramadan**, adults fast between sunrise and sunset.</li></ul>
Rastafarians	<ul><li>Mainly vegetarian, although some eat fish.</li><li>Rastafarians do not eat pork.</li><li>Dairy products that do not contain rennet.</li></ul>

▲ Find out about a child's food requirements from your supervisor or the child's parents.

Vegetarians and vegans

Some people do not eat any meat or fish. This can be part of their religious beliefs or because they do not agree with killing or using animals. If you are caring for a child who is a vegetarian or vegan, you will need to ask the parents or your supervisor for help to make sure that meals are nutritious and interesting. Vegetarians will eat dairy products such as milk, yoghurt, cheese and eggs, but will not eat meat or fish. Vegans do not eat anything that comes from an animal, even if it does not mean killing the animal – for example, they do not eat milk, cheese, eggs or honey.

Activity

Find the five foods in this list that would be suitable for a child who is a vegetarian:

- cheese
- hamburger
- tomatoes
- yoghurt
- bread
- fishfingers
- lentils
- tuna.

Summary

- Some children will have special food requirements for religious, cultural or medical reasons.
- Adults must always ask parents about their child's food requirements.
- It is essential to respect parents' beliefs.

Food allergies and medical conditions

Some foods can make children ill or make a medical condition worse. This is why it is essential to know children's food requirements and to check food labels carefully.

Finding out about food requirements

Finding out about what children should and should not be given is essential as some foods can make certain children very ill. Most settings ask parents to fill in a form that includes questions about their child's health as well as any food requirements that their child may have.

Food allergies

Some children are allergic to specific foods. Some foods can cause mild allergic reactions such as eczema, but some foods can trigger very violent reactions. This is why adults should always be present when children are given food.

Signs of a violent allergic reaction can include:

- swelling of the lips
- rashes and welts appearing on the skin
- coughing and difficulty in breathing.

If you think that a child is having an allergic reaction, you must GET HELP.

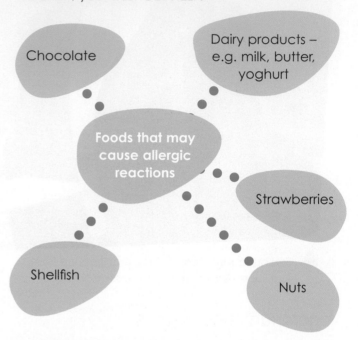

Diabetes	Children with diabetes can become ill if their diets are not followed. Most diabetics have to limit their sugar intake and this may mean children are not allowed ordinary chocolate and sweets. They may need to eat at certain times of the day, otherwise they quickly become ill. Some children with diabetes may also need to have an injection before they eat.
Coeliacs	Children with coeliac disease cannot eat gluten, which is found in wheat and oats. Wheat flour is in many types of foods such as bread, biscuits, pasta and cakes. Children with coeliac disease may bring in their own biscuits and other food.
Nut allergy	Some children have violent reactions if they eat nuts.
Milk allergy	Some babies cannot be given ordinary formula milk. Children can also be allergic to cow's milk and, instead, have alternatives. Children who are allergic to cow's milk may also have problems with yoghurt, butter and other products made with cow's milk.

▲ Some of these children have special food requirements. Why is it important that they are not made to feel 'different'?

Activity

Choose one of the following children. See if your partner can guess which one you are by asking questions about what you can eat.

Sandra   a child with coeliac disease

Andrea   a child who only eats vegetarian food

Jack   a child who is Jewish

Rahima   a child who has a dairy-free diet

Summary

- Some foods can make certain children very ill.
- Always check before giving children any food or drink.
- Read labels on foods carefully.

End of unit summary

End of unit task: Menu

Look carefully at this menu, which is for children over two years old.

1 For each snack or meal, work out the nutrients that the child would have.

2 Does this menu lack any nutrients?

3 List the foods on this menu that some children might not be able to have. Why?

4 How could you improve this menu to ensure a child would get enough nutrients?

5 Design your own menu that will help give a child a balanced diet.

Breakfast

Toast and butter

Milk

Mid-morning snack and drink

Biscuit and orange squash

Lunch

Ham sandwiches

Chocolate biscuit

Glass of orange squash

Mid-afternoon snack and drink

Cheese and biscuits

Orange squash

Tea

Bacon and cheese potato pie

Yoghurt

Glass of milk

Back to the real world

You should now be able to help prepare and serve food. You are also planning to take a food hygiene course leading to a certificate.

1 Can you give an example of a food that is high in carbohydrates?

2 Can you give an example of a food that is high in protein?

3 Can you list three foods that should not be given to babies?

My story

Kelly

Before doing this course, I did not really think about what children ate. Now I know that what children eat is really important. I am also thinking more about what I eat as well. I was surprised to find out that babies must not be weaned until they are six months old. On the course, we also found out about how to prevent food poisoning. Afterwards I went home and sorted out our fridge! I always wash my hands now and have a big thing about keeping uncooked meat away from other foods. I have just started in a nursery and I am going on a food hygiene course.

Glossary

antibodies Cells made in the body to fight off infections

expressed milk Breast milk that is stored for use later

growth spurt When a child grows very quickly in a short space of time

halal Food that is prepared according to Islamic dietary laws

kosher Food that is prepared according to Jewish dietary laws

Ramadan An Islamic period of fasting during daylight hours

Unit 4 Health and safety

Adults who work with children have a responsibility to protect them. This means preventing infections as well as accidents. Adults also need to know what to do if a child does have an accident.

This unit will help you understand what causes some infections and also how infections can spread. You will learn about practical ways of preventing the spread of infection. The unit also looks at ways in which adults can help prevent accidents as well as what you should do if there is an emergency or an accident. The unit covers the following:

- how to prevent the spread of infection
- how to store and handle food safely

- how to ensure home and group settings are safe and healthy
- basic first aid principles and actions to take in an emergency.

The topics you will find in this unit are:

- How infection is spread
- Preventing the spread of infection
- Storing and handling food safely
- Identifying potential hazards
- Potential hazards in group care settings
- Preventing accidents
- Health and safety procedures
- First aid principles
- Actions in an emergency

In the real world

It is your first day in a nursery. You are surprised to see that the gate is locked and that you have to sign in when you get there. When you go into the baby room, you notice that the staff use disposable gloves and aprons to change nappies. Your placement supervisor also talks you through the health and safety procedures. You wonder why so much fuss is being made!

By the end of this unit, you will understand why adults working with children have to take so much care. You will learn about ways of preventing accidents and infections. You will also know what you must do if a child does have an accident.

How infection is spread

Babies and young children can pick up infections easily because their bodies find it harder to fight germs. Germs are all around us. Many of them are harmless and some even help our bodies, but some can attack the body.

The word 'germs' is often used when talking about infection, but there are actually several different groups of germs.

- **Bacteria** cause many illnesses, including ear infections and bronchitis. Some bacteria can be killed by **antibiotics**.
- **Viruses** cause illnesses like common colds, coughs and flu. Viruses cannot be killed by antibiotics.

- **Fungal infections** are caused by fungus (mushrooms are a type of fungus). Athlete's foot and thrush are common fungal infections.
- **Parasites**: as well as germs, the body can also be attacked by parasites. Parasites live on or in the body. Head lice and threadworms are common parasites.

Bacteria, viruses and fungi **love** warmth and moisture.

How germs enter the human body

There are three ways germs can get into our bodies.

- **Being swallowed (ingestion)**

  We can take in bacteria, fungi and parasites by swallowing them. They may be on food that we eat or on objects that we touch – these germs are then passed to the mouth by the hands.

- **Being breathed in (inhalation)**

  Droplets of moist air often contain viruses and bacteria. Coughing and sneezing can spread infection through the air.

- **Through a cut or damage to the skin (inoculation)**

  Bacteria can get through skin when it is damaged because of a cut, blister or burn.

Preventing the spread of infection

It is impossible for settings to be completely free of bacteria and viruses, but there are steps that must be taken to prevent the spread of infection.

Ways of preventing germs from getting into the body

Inhalation (being breathed in)	• Make sure rooms are not hot and stuffy (no warmer than 22°C). • Leave a window slightly open to get some fresh air. • Encourage children to put their hands over their mouths when coughing and sneezing.
Ingestion (being swallowed)	• Germs are often found on hands. Wash hands before eating and keep hands clean to stop germs from being swallowed. • Wear disposable gloves and aprons to stop germs from getting onto clothes and hands. • Clean toys and equipment to stop germs from reaching hands. • Cover food and cook it properly to stop bacteria, fungi or parasites getting in through swallowing.
Inoculation (cuts or damaged skin)	• Wash and cover cuts, grazes and blisters.

Common infections and ways to prevent them from spreading

Coughs and colds
- Make sure rooms are not too hot and stuffy.
- Make sure children put hands over mouths when coughing.
- Use tissues rather than handkerchiefs.
- Make sure children wash hands after blowing noses.

Threadworms
- Keep nails short.
- Wash hands before handling food.
- Use nail brushes.
- Wash hands after using the toilet.

Head lice
- Keep long hair tied back.
- Check for head lice regularly.
- Comb hair thoroughly.
- Treat head lice when necessary.

Stomach upsets
- Use disposable gloves and aprons when cleaning up.
- Make sure clothes and aprons are washed.
- Do not let rooms become hot and stuffy.
- Make sure anyone who has had a stomach upset does not come in until they are better.
- Make sure the kitchen is cleaned thoroughly.
- Clean cutlery, plates and cups thoroughly.
- Make sure food is cooked thoroughly and stored properly.
- Make sure the toilets and bathroom areas are clean.

Activity

One of the rooms in the nursery is very hot and stuffy. Many of the children have coughs and colds.

1 With a partner think of three things you could do to prevent the infections from spreading.

2 Compare your answers with the rest of the group.

Summary

- Germs multiply quickly when it is warm and moist.
- Germs enter the body through swallowing, breathing in and through the skin.
- Different types of germs and infections include bacteria, viruses, fungal infections and parasites.
- Common infections include coughs, colds, threadworms, head lice and stomach upsets.

Preventing the spread of infection

Keeping settings clean and taking steps to prevent infection are as important as providing fun things for children to do. There are many practical steps that can be taken to help prevent the spread of infection. Remember to read pages 68–69 about preventing infections from food as well.

Using and storing cleaning materials

To prevent germs from spreading, equipment, toys and surfaces need to be cleaned thoroughly. Most settings use cleaning products that have some bleach or disinfectant in them. These can kill bacteria but need to be used carefully because they are poisonous.

- Read labels on cleaning products.
- Store cleaning materials in locked cupboards away from children.
- Do not mix cleaning products.
- Wear rubber/disposable gloves when using cleaning materials.
- Do not use aerosols near children. They can trigger asthma attacks.

Steps to prevent the spread of infection indoors

What to do	Why
Wash hands	Germs can often be on the hands and then be swallowed when the hands touch the mouth. Look back at page 28 to remind yourself of when hands need to be washed.
Clean and wash toys and small equipment	Babies and young children may touch toys and then put their hands in their mouths.
Wash floors, tables and kitchen surfaces	Germs can spread to food or toys and equipment from these surfaces. Children may also touch tables and floor.
Tidy up properly	Tidying makes it easier to clean properly.
Wipe up spills	Germs love damp areas. Spills can also cause accidents.
Keep toilets and bathrooms clean	Threadworms and bacteria can spread to hands from toilets and bathroom areas. Wear disposable gloves when cleaning.
Use paper towels	Germs can be passed to the next person if you use ordinary towels.
Empty bins	Waste can overflow onto the floor and cause germs to spread more easily.
Wear disposable gloves and aprons when changing nappies, clearing up sick, etc.	Germs can get onto the hands and be passed on. Throw away nappies and towels with sick on them in special bins.
Supervise children when handling animals	Animals may bite if they are being annoyed and germs can enter the skin when it is damaged.
Keep animals away from food	Germs can spread from animals to children and to food.

Preventing the spread of infection outdoors

Children can pick up infections outdoors. Look at the steps needed to make sure that this does not happen.

Steps to prevent the spread of infection outdoors

- Supervise children very carefully when they are outside.
- Make sure children wash their hands after playing outside.
- Keep the lid on sand pits.
- Prevent dogs from straying into outdoor areas.
- Discourage children from picking up feathers, plants and litter.
- Make sure children have washed their hands before eating.

- **Toys and equipment** need to be kept clean so children do not get germs on their hands when they touch the equipment.
- Dogs and cats often mess in **soil, sand and grass**. There is a danger of children becoming ill because the **larvae** from the worms in dogs and cats can be swallowed. Soil also contains bacteria.
- **Animals** can sometimes bite children if they are provoked. A bite can cause germs to enter through the broken skin. Birds' feathers and nests may contain germs that make children ill.
- Sometimes little children pick up **litter** that has fallen on to the ground. The litter is likely to be dirty and children may then put their hands in their mouths.

Activity

You are about to do a cooking activity with some children. When you go into the kitchen, you find that someone has spilled some milk on the work surface and a cat is licking it up. You also notice that the bin is very full and the lid won't shut.

1 What do you need to do before you start the activity?

2 What do the children need to do before they start the activity?

Summary

- Washing hands is essential to prevent the spread of infections.
- Cleaning is an important way to prevent infections from spreading.
- Cleaning materials must be stored away from children.

Storing and handling food safely

Food poisoning caused by swallowing germs is a real threat. Children can become very ill and sometimes die from food poisoning.

Handling foods

- Use separate chopping boards and knives for raw and cooked foods.
- Wash your hands after touching raw meat and fish.
- Wash your hands frequently while cooking.
- If tasting foods, wash the spoon or fork before using it again.

Getting ready to handle foods

Before handling foods you should:

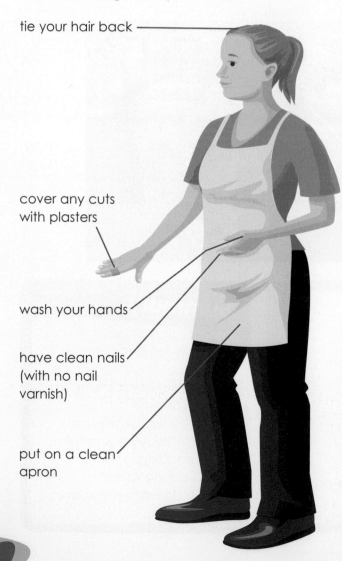

tie your hair back

cover any cuts with plasters

wash your hands

have clean nails (with no nail varnish)

put on a clean apron

Do you remember?

On pages 68–69 we looked at how to prepare food safely and hygienically.

- Can you remember five ways to prevent bacteria from reaching food?
- How can bacteria be slowed down?
- How can bacteria be killed off?

Use-by dates

Before cooking or serving food, you should always check the use-by dates. Food that is no longer in date must be thrown away. Bacteria on some foods can gradually build up to dangerous levels.

- Check how long food can be kept once opened, for example tomato ketchup and orange juice. Most food needs to be refrigerated once opened.
- Use cooked foods quickly – usually eat within three days.
- Do not reheat food more than once.
- Make sure fruit and vegetables are fresh and not bruised or limp.
- Do not use potatoes that are green.
- Do not use meat or fish that smells strongly.
- Check how long frozen food has been kept before using it.
- Check that bread and cakes are still fresh – they can become mouldy!

Checklist for the kitchen
- ✔ Kitchen is tidy
- ✔ Kitchen surfaces have been cleaned
- ✔ Bin is not full
- ✔ Plates, cutlery and cups are properly washed
- ✔ Sink is clean
- ✔ Aprons are clean
- ✔ Tea towels are clean
- ✔ First aid kit is available

Storing food

Food should always be kept wrapped or covered to prevent bacteria from getting onto it. The table on page 93 shows the best way to store different types of food.

Food	How to wrap/cover	Where to store
Dry foods (pasta, rice, biscuits, tea)	In an airtight container	In a cool, dry cupboard
Bread, cakes	Wrapped or put in tin	In a bread bin or tin
Dairy products (milk, cheese)	Wrapped or packaged	In a refrigerator
Fresh meat and fish	Wrapped or covered and kept away from cooked foods and dairy products	In a refrigerator
Cooked foods	Wrapped or covered and kept away from raw meat	In a refrigerator (kept at 0–5°C)
Fruit and vegetables	Taken out of plastic bags	In a cool, dry place or at the bottom of a refrigerator
Canned foods	Check tin is not dented or damaged	In a dry cupboard
Frozen foods (ice-cream, meat)	Wrapped or packaged	In a freezer (kept at –18°C)

Bottom shelf
uncooked meat
and fish

Top shelves
dairy products,
cooked foods

Salad drawers
fruit and
vegetables

Activity

Look at the following foods:

- a packet of fresh lamb mince
- a packet of frozen peas
- some cooked ham
- a pot of yoghurt
- an opened bottle of ketchup
- a packet of biscuits
- some potatoes.

1   Where should you store each of them?
2   What checks would you need to make before eating or cooking each of the foods?

Summary

- Foods need to be stored correctly.
- Foods need to be checked before being cooked and eaten.
- Fridges and freezers need to be at the correct temperatures.

Identifying potential hazards

In order to keep children safe, we must be able to identify and deal with hazards. One of the main ways to keep children safe is to supervise them and look out for hazards. Look at how the safety needs of children change as they grow:

Age	Needs	Role of adult
0–2 years	<ul><li>No understanding of danger</li><li>Toys and objects are put into mouth</li><li>May easily trip and fall</li><li>Can pull objects down onto themselves</li><li>May choke on food</li></ul>	<ul><li>Stay next to children at all times (constant supervision).</li><li>Never leave children alone, even for a short time.</li><li>Check toys to see if they are suitable.</li></ul>
2–4 years	<ul><li>Little understanding of danger</li><li>Keen to explore and do things for themselves</li><li>May copy things that adults do – e.g. try out medicine, smoke</li></ul>	<ul><li>Stay near children.</li><li>Check toys to see if they are suitable.</li><li>Watch out when children are very quiet or very noisy!</li><li>Do not let children go near roads.</li><li>Do not leave children alone near ponds or water.</li></ul>
4–8 years	<ul><li>Some awareness of danger</li><li>May copy things they see adults do</li><li>May get overexcited when playing</li></ul>	<ul><li>Children can play by themselves, but adults must stay nearby.</li><li>Listen out for signs that children are arguing.</li><li>Cross roads safely with children.</li></ul>

Hazards inside the home

There are hazards to look out for everywhere – even in the home.

Bathroom
- Children can drown in the bath.
- Keep cleaning materials out of reach of children.
- Lock any medicines in a cupboard.
- Hot water can scald children's skin.

Bedrooms
- Children enjoy bouncing on beds, but may fall.
- Plugs need covering.
- Toys must be right for the age of the child.
- Cuddly toys must be safe.
- Check upstairs windows are locked.

Kitchen
- Never leave children alone.
- Keep children away from cookers and knives.
- Lock cleaning materials in a cupboard.
- Keep irons, kettles and deep fat fryers out of children's reach.
- Do not let wires dangle.

Stairs
- Supervise toddlers on stairs.
- Use stair gates.
- Do not let children play on stairs.
- Keep stairs clear of toys and objects.

Living/dining room
- Toys must be suitable for the age of the children.
- Cover sockets.
- Keep wires and flexes out of children's reach.
- Keep cigarettes and lighters out of children's reach.
- Keep electrical equipment out of children's reach.
- High chairs must be stable.
- Hot drinks must not be left around.
- Use fire guards.
- Tables with sharp edges may need plastic corners.

Outdoor hazards

Children enjoy being outside, but there are some hazards adults need to look out for.

Insects
- In the summer, wasps and other insects can be attracted to bins and food.
- Make sure children play away from bins.

Strangers
- Although most strangers will not harm children, they are still a possible hazard.
- Make sure you can see children at all times.
- Closely supervise toddlers and young children at all times.

Traffic
- Do not leave children alone near roads.
- Use reins and harnesses with very young children to stop them straying into the road.

Outdoor hazards

Dogs
- Dogs can frighten young children and can sometimes jump up at them.
- Dogs' mess can contain worms which, if swallowed, can make children ill.

Litter
- In some public places, such as parks, children may find litter.
- Supervise very young children to make sure they do not pick up litter.
- Look out for broken glass and syringes that can cause accidents.

Play equipment
- Many parks have play areas with slides and swings.
- Check that these are suitable for the age of the children.
- Check that they are in good condition and are not dirty.

Hazards in the garden

Some children are lucky and have a garden to play in. There are still hazards to look out for, however.

Toddlers could escape through gaps in fences

Children could fall down steps and hurt themselves

Some plants may be poisonous

Forks or other gardening equipment could fall on children or cut them

Weed killer could poison children

Children could fall and drown in a pond

Activity

Look at the picture of the garden above.

What would you need to do to make it safe for a child to play there?

Summary

- Good supervision can prevent accidents from happening.
- A tidy environment can help prevent accidents.
- Checking for possible hazards will help prevent accidents.

Potential hazards in group care settings

As well as knowing about the hazards in children's own homes, it is important to be able to identify hazards in group care settings such as nurseries, out-of-school clubs and play groups.

Indoor hazards

Good supervision is extremely important in group care settings as well as indoors. Accidents can happen very quickly indoors, especially when groups of children are playing together. In some cases, it is useful to look at the layout of a setting to ensure it is not likely to cause accidents.

Outdoor areas

Staff must check outdoor areas before children go outside. Groups of children playing outside may bump into each other, so good supervision is essential. Look at the box below and see if you can spot some of the same hazards that are found in home settings.

Other children

When there are several children playing, they may bump into each other or push each other over. Children may also throw or wave equipment in the air as part of their play. This can cause accidents. Because of this, babies and toddlers are not normally put with older children.

Water

Children can actually drown in just a few centimetres of water. This means that any water activity needs to be carefully supervised. Any spills also need to be wiped up.

Kitchen area

As in the home setting, kitchens are very dangerous places for children. Most settings put up a safety gate to stop children from going into the kitchen. If cooking with children, keep them away from hot stoves, kettles and sharp knives.

Sand

Good supervision of sand is essential as, if thrown into a child's eye, it can cause eye problems. It also needs to be swept up immediately if it gets on the floor as it is very slippery.

Toilet and bathroom areas

These can become slippery if wet. Wipe up any spills and make sure that these areas are clean. Do not allow children to play in toilet areas.

Toys and equipment

Toys and equipment need to be checked for damage. They also need to be checked to make sure they are suitable for the age of children playing with them. Toddlers can swallow very small parts. Older children can break equipment such as tricycles if they are too large for them.

Doors

Doors need to be easy to open in case of an emergency. Children must not play with doors. Staff should carefully supervise areas near doors in case children try to get out or trap their fingers.

Poisonous plants

Gaps in fencing that may allow children to stray out or strangers to get in

Children becoming overexcited in their play

Children walking in front of slides and swings

Hazards in outdoor areas

Children pushing each other on slides

Children using equipment incorrectly – e.g. standing up on tricycles

Litter

Dogs' and cats' mess

Dirty, broken or cracked equipment

Activity

Design an information sheet that could be used to check for hazards in an outdoor play area, garden or park.

Summary

- Staff must check outdoor areas before children go outdoors.
- Children must be kept out of the kitchen.
- Spills of sand and water must be cleared up immediately.

Preventing accidents

Many accidents can be prevented by good supervision and using safety equipment. **Good supervision** means actively looking after children and, in the case of babies and toddlers, watching them constantly. Good supervision also means listening out in case there are signs that children are overexcited or bored.

Toys, equipment and play areas should be regularly checked for hazards. Look out for cracks, rust and missing parts in toys and equipment.

Homes and group care settings use safety equipment to prevent accidents. It is important to follow manufacturers' instructions and to actually use the safety equipment.

▲ Safety equipment, such as safety gates, helps to prevent accidents in both home and group care settings.

Safety equipment	Where used	Why
Electric socket covers	Home and group	• To prevent babies and children from poking fingers and objects into sockets
Safety gates	Home and group	• To stop babies and young children from climbing up or falling down stairs
Safety corners	Home and group	• These are put on table corners to stop children from hitting their eyes
Harnesses and reins	Home and group	• To stop babies and toddlers from falling out of high chairs • To stop toddlers and young children from running into the road
Safety catches	Home and group	• To stop children from opening cupboards or drawers
Car seats	Home	• To protect babies and children in case of a car accident
Cooker guard	Home and group	• To stop children from pulling saucepans from the cooker on to themselves.

Activity

Choose three pieces of safety equipment from the table above and state in which room you would expect to find them.

Look back to the picture on page 94 to help you.

Summary

- Accidents can happen very quickly.
- Children in group care settings need constant supervision.
- Safety equipment can prevent accidents if used properly.

Health and safety procedures

Health and safety are so important that there are laws and regulations to protect everyone. Settings will also have health and safety policies to make sure the setting is a safe place for everyone.

Health and Safety at Work Act (1974)

This is an important law which is designed to protect everyone in the workplace. It also makes employees responsible for their own safety as well as that of others. Under this law:

- employees must use the health and safety equipment provided – e.g. use disposable aprons or safety gates

- employees must report any hazards, accidents or dangers to their employer – e.g. tell your employer if you spot a broken toy
- employees must not do anything that may harm others – e.g. do not have hot drinks near children.

Policies and procedures

Every group care setting will have a health and safety policy. The policy should explain the procedures staff need to follow in order to keep themselves and children safe. It is important that you read the policy carefully so that you know how to report hazards and accidents and what to do if there is an emergency.

Types of procedure

Reporting hazards

Settings may have a procedure to follow if you spot a hazard such as a broken toy or a hole in the carpet. It is important to report hazards so that you can help prevent accidents.

Storing chemicals

Settings may have a procedure that explains where poisonous items such as cleaning materials must be stored.

Disposing of waste materials

Human waste such as urine, faeces or sick can spread infection. Group care settings will have a procedure to make sure adults wear protective aprons and gloves and also that they put this waste in a separate bin (this may be a yellow bin).

Reporting accidents

All accidents have to be reported accurately. Parents must be informed if their child has had an accident; even if it is a minor one such as a grazed knee, as the child might need other treatment later.

ACCIDENT REPORT FORM

Name: *Roshida Abdullah*	
Date: *14/06/09*	Time: *3.40pm*
Details of accident:	
Roshida fell off the slide and bumped the back of her head	
Location:	*Red slide – garden*
Details of injury:	*Slight bump on head*
Treatment:	*Cold water compress*
Given by:	*Sarah Donald*
Signature:	*Sarah Donald*

Emergency procedures

Everyone in the setting must know what to do if there is a fire or if the building needs to be evacuated in an emergency. Most settings have practices to make sure that staff and children can recognise the alarm and leave the building quickly.

Settings should also have notices in each room explaining the procedure. These would cover the following.

- **Assembly area**: This is likely to be somewhere away from the building where a register can be taken.
- **Use the nearest exit**: This means that adults and children move out of the way of danger as quickly as possible. You should always know where the nearest exit is.
- **Do not stop to collect personal belongings**: The most important thing is to leave quickly.
- **Remain calm**: It is important for adults to be calm so children do not become upset. The alarms may be loud so children may need comforting.
- **Take a register or roll call**: This is to make sure that everyone is out of the building.

Manufacturers' instructions

Many pieces of equipment are used in homes and in group care settings. Some accidents happen because adults do not follow the manufacturer's instructions. For example, they might let an older child play on a toy designed for a much younger child.

Equipment	Look out for	Why
Slides and climbing frames	• Age or weight restrictions • Fixing instructions	• Equipment may break. • Child may fall off.
Microwave	• No metal allowed • Cooking and standing times	• Microwave may break. • Food may not be properly cooked through.

Always read and follow the manufacturer's instructions.

Keep the manufacturer's instructions and store them safely when you buy new equipment.

WIZARD NURSERY EVACUATION PROCEDURE

Your assembly point is:

DUKE STREET PLAYGROUND

What you must do in the case of a fire or other emergency:

When the fire alarm sounds

- The senior person or authorised deputy will take charge of any evacuation and ensure no one is left in the area.
- Leave the building as instructed by the nearest exit and report to the person in charge of the assembly point at the place indicated above. A roll call will be taken.

Remember

- Keep calm.
- Use the nearest available exit.
- Do not use the lift.
- Do not re-enter the building for any reason until the safety officer gives you permission.

Activity

Zara works in a nursery and is moaning that her manager insists the safety gate in the kitchen is always used. She thinks it's a waste of time, especially as the lock doesn't work properly.

What would you say to her and why?

Summary

- Employees have a duty to use the safety equipment provided.
- Everyone in a setting needs to read health and safety policies.
- Evacuation drills help people know what to do in an emergency.
- Following the manufacturer's instructions can prevent accidents.

First aid principles

All adults who work with children need to know what to do if a child is dangerously ill or badly injured.

The aim of any first aid treatment is to keep the injured person alive and to prevent their condition from becoming any worse. You should not give first aid treatment unless you have been on a first aid course. The only exception to this rule is if it is a real emergency and there is no qualified first aider nearby.

Find out who has first aid training in the setting

Every setting should have at least one person who has had recent first aid training. It is important that you know who this is. Settings should also have a first aid kit, and many have more than one. First aid kits are normally green with a white cross on them.

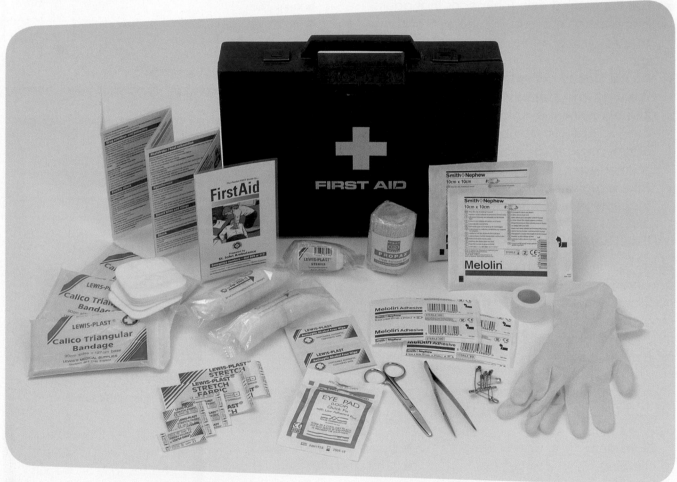

▲ Find out what's in your setting's first aid kit.
Do not remove scissors or anything else from a first aid kit unnecessarily.

What to do if a child has an accident

Accidents can happen very quickly. Whatever the type of accident, you will need to respond quickly, remain calm and think carefully.

Stay calm and think

Quickly look around

- Is the child in any further danger?
- Is there any danger to you or to other children?

Check for signs that the child needs first aid

- Not moving or unconscious
- Difficulty in breathing or is not breathing
- Glazed expression
- Cold and clammy skin
- Blue lips and nails
- Arms or legs at an awkward angle
- Drowsy and/or vomiting after a blow to the head
- Bleeding heavily.

When in doubt always seek help.

GET HELP immediately

Stay with the child and shout or call for help.

Dial 999 or 112

Getting emergency help

Getting emergency help quickly may save a child's life. You may need to dial 999 or 112 to get help. This service is only to be used in real emergencies. The operator will ask you several questions and it is important that you remain calm enough to answer them:

- your name and the phone number you are dialling from
- the location of the accident – it is important that you are accurate so that the ambulance or emergency services can find you quickly
- what has happened – this helps the emergency team know what to expect
- what you have done so far to treat the emergency.

The operator may also give you advice while the ambulance is on the way. If possible, send someone outside (not a child) to guide the ambulance crew.

Reassuring children

If a child is conscious, it is important to reassure them that help is coming and that they will be all right. They may be scared and in pain and need to feel that an adult is in control. Unless the child is in further danger, do not move them, but wait with them. If there are other children around, remember to reassure them and, if possible, arrange for them to go elsewhere.

Activity

A four-year-old child has fallen out of a tree in a park. Her left arm is at an awkward angle and she is complaining that she feels dizzy and sick. Another adult who is a first aider has told you to call an ambulance.

What information will you need to remember?

Summary

- In an emergency you must stay calm and reassure the child.
- Unless you are a trained first aider, you should always try to seek help.
- Signs that a child needs emergency help include unconsciousness, difficulty in breathing and heavy bleeding.
- 999 or 112 calls should only be used in real emergencies.

Actions in an emergency

Reading about first aid treatments is not the same as having proper training. For you to work with children, you must have some first aid training that looks specifically at the needs of children. This is called paediatric first aid training. (If you are working in England, check with your tutor that this training meets the requirements of the Early Years Foundation Stage.)

Your first action in an emergency will always be to get a trained first aider.

Dealing with a child who is not breathing and is unconscious

A child who is not breathing and is unconscious will need to be resuscitated. You need to be trained to carry out mouth-to-mouth resuscitation.

Dealing with an unconscious child

A child who is unconscious, but breathing, should be put into the recovery position to help them breathe. Seek emergency help immediately.

Dealing with other incidents

- Do not move children unless they are in further danger or are unconscious.
- Do not give children who have had a major accident any food or drink before emergency help arrives.
- Remain calm.
- Reassure the child.

Dealing with minor accidents

Many children have small bumps, grazes or bruises. You should reassure them and then take them to a first aider in your setting.

Some children are allergic to plasters and certain medicines. This means that you should never treat or give children any medicines by yourself.

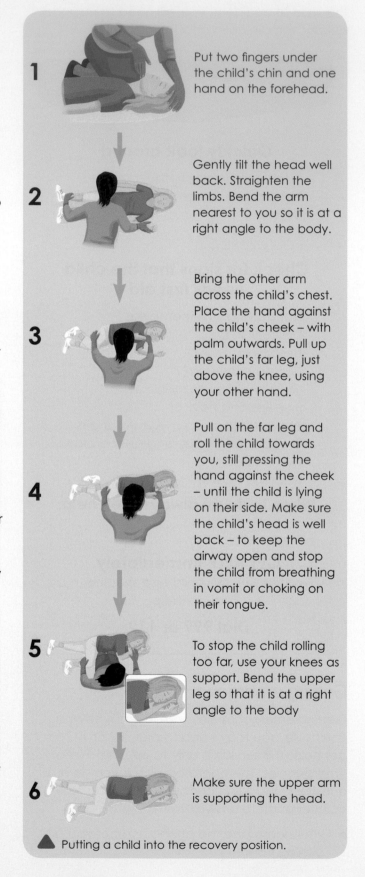

1 Put two fingers under the child's chin and one hand on the forehead.

2 Gently tilt the head well back. Straighten the limbs. Bend the arm nearest to you so it is at a right angle to the body.

3 Bring the other arm across the child's chest. Place the hand against the child's cheek – with palm outwards. Pull up the child's far leg, just above the knee, using your other hand.

4 Pull on the far leg and roll the child towards you, still pressing the hand against the cheek – until the child is lying on their side. Make sure the child's head is well back – to keep the airway open and stop the child from breathing in vomit or choking on their tongue.

5 To stop the child rolling too far, use your knees as support. Bend the upper leg so that it is at a right angle to the body

6 Make sure the upper arm is supporting the head.

▲ Putting a child into the recovery position.

Incident	Signs and symptoms	Action
Head injury	• Bump on head • Drowsiness • Vomiting	• If the child is drowsy or vomiting, seek emergency help immediately.
Poisoning	• Vomiting • Child in pain • Child is poorly • You see what has been taken	• Ask the child what they have eaten. • Watch for signs of losing consciousness. • Do not make the child vomit. • Do not make the child drink. • Seek emergency help. • Give the suspected poison to the emergency team.
Choking	• Child is coughing and gasping for breath	• Hold the child so their head is downwards, this can be over your knees. • Slap firmly with the flat of the hand between the shoulder blades. • Seek emergency help if no improvement.
Cuts and wounds	• Heavy bleeding	• Place a clean pad over the wound. • Press and hold. • Seek emergency help.
Fractures	• Awkward angle of arm or leg • Swelling • Loss of movement • Pain	• Keep the child still and reassure them. • Get a first aider to come to help you. • Use a scarf or sling to steady the limb.

Reporting accidents

If a child has any type of accident in a setting, parents must be told about it. Most settings will send home a slip which tells the parents what has happened and how the child has been treated (see page 100 for an example). This is important because sometimes the child may become ill later on.

Emergency contact details

Every setting should keep records of how to contact parents in an emergency. This information is usually given by parents when their child first joins a setting. It should be checked and updated regularly.

Summary

- Do not give children who have been involved in a major accident any food or drink.
- Unconscious children should be put in the recovery position.
- Parents need to know if any type of accident has taken place.
- Emergency contact details need to be checked and updated regularly.

Activity

A group of children is playing outdoors. One child falls over. She has grazed her knee, bumped her head and is sobbing.

What would you do next?

End of unit summary

Getting ready for assessment

The assignment for this unit requires you to be able to identify some hazards in different settings and to show that you know how you could prevent them.

You also need to know what might happen to children if no precautions were taken. Finally, you must be able to write a few sentences explaining why adults must take health and safety very seriously.

End of unit task: Health and safety poster

In pairs, copy out and complete these charts.

Use them to make a poster to help people learn about health and safety.

Hazards in home setting

Hazard	Why	Action
Stairs	Children might fall	Put up stair gates
Cooker		
Upstairs open window		
Medicine cabinet	Children might swallow medicines	
Electric sockets/equipment		
Hot iron		
Mugs of tea or coffee		
Hot water in taps	Children might be scalded	
Sharp knives		
Cleaning fluids left out		
Broken toys		
Toys with very small parts		

Outdoor hazards

Hazard	Why	Action
Poisonous plants		
Litter on ground		
Ponds and canals		
Swimming pools	Children might swim out of depth	
Wasps and bees		
Broken fences		
Dogs' and cats' mess		
Broken equipment		
Dogs off their leads		
Roads		

Spread of infections

Hazard	Why	Action
Hot and stuffy room		
Out-of-date food		
Dirty kitchen		
Staff not washing hands before preparing food		
Children not washing hands before eating		

Back to the real world

You should know and understand how infection can spread and why it is important to wear disposable gloves, aprons and to wash hands. You should also be aware of hazards indoors and outdoors that you must think about when looking after children. You should also know what to do if a child had an accident.

1 Can you list the three ways in which germs can enter the human body?

2 Can you think of three ways in which germs can be prevented from entering the body?

3 List three hazards that you might find indoors and outdoors in a home setting.

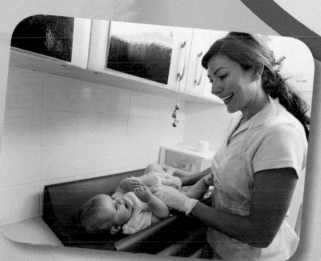

Glossary

antibiotics A type of medicine that kills bacteria

bacteria A type of germ

fungal infection A type of infection

larvae An insect that has hatched from an egg before transforming into the adult; e.g. a maggot will become a fly

parasites Tiny animals that live on other animals or humans

viruses A type of germ

My story

Hayley

I am a deputy manager at a day care centre. I am responsible for heath and safety. Each time a new student or member of staff joins us, I always go through our policy. As part of my job, I carry out risk assessments. Risk assessment means looking at activities, areas and equipment and thinking about whether there are any dangers. If there are, I then have to think of ways of making them safer. For example, we now have a locked cupboard where the cleaners keep their cleaning products.

Unit 5 Care of children

Looking after children also means making sure they are comfortable. They need to be washed, clothed and given opportunities to be active as well as to sleep. This is quite a responsibility as children can become poorly if their needs are not met properly.

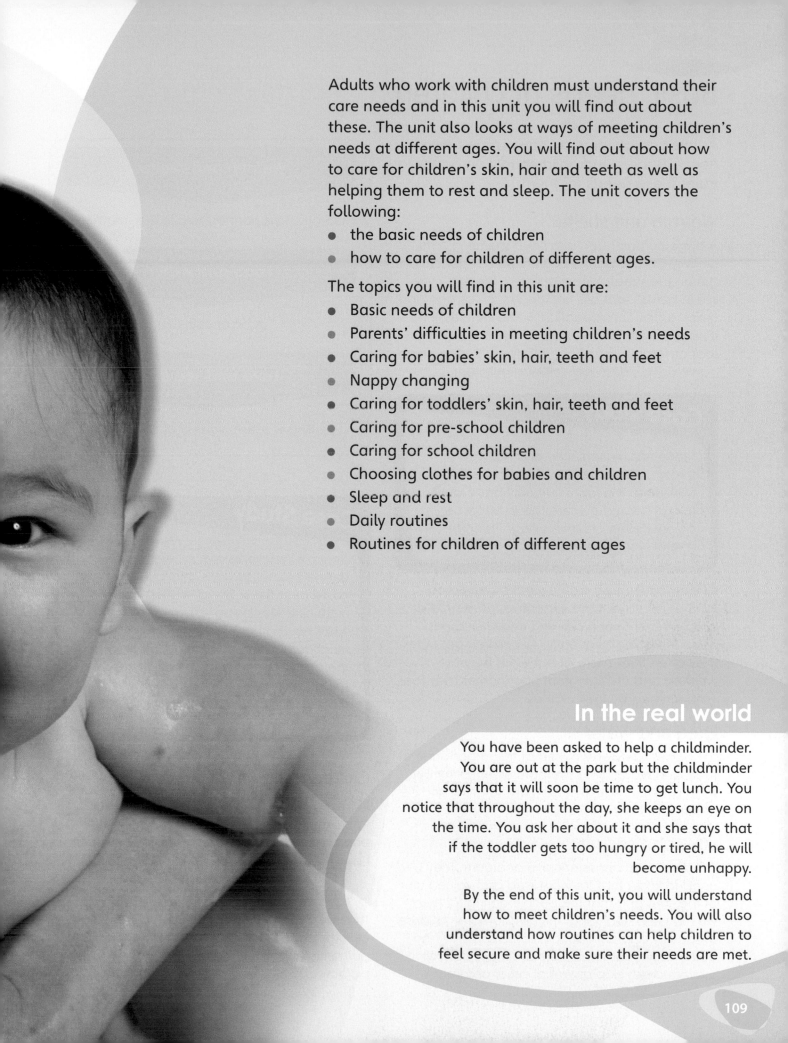

Adults who work with children must understand their care needs and in this unit you will find out about these. The unit also looks at ways of meeting children's needs at different ages. You will find out about how to care for children's skin, hair and teeth as well as helping them to rest and sleep. The unit covers the following:

- the basic needs of children
- how to care for children of different ages.

The topics you will find in this unit are:

- Basic needs of children
- Parents' difficulties in meeting children's needs
- Caring for babies' skin, hair, teeth and feet
- Nappy changing
- Caring for toddlers' skin, hair, teeth and feet
- Caring for pre-school children
- Caring for school children
- Choosing clothes for babies and children
- Sleep and rest
- Daily routines
- Routines for children of different ages

In the real world

You have been asked to help a childminder. You are out at the park but the childminder says that it will soon be time to get lunch. You notice that throughout the day, she keeps an eye on the time. You ask her about it and she says that if the toddler gets too hungry or tired, he will become unhappy.

By the end of this unit, you will understand how to meet children's needs. You will also understand how routines can help children to feel secure and make sure their needs are met.

Basic needs of children

Adults and children all have some basic needs. Babies and children rely on adults to meet these needs for them.

Warmth and shelter

A basic human need is to have **shelter** in order to survive. Children in this country do not generally live on the streets. Some children, though, may live in homes that are not ideal, such as bed and breakfast accommodation. Some families find it hard to heat their homes or may have homes that are damp or in poor condition. Poor housing can lead to illness, especially in children.

Warmth and shelter

Somewhere comfortable to live; clothes

Food and water

A balanced diet

Love and security

Feeling wanted, valued and cared for

Case study

Maria has two children and has been thrown out of the flat that belongs to her boyfriend. The local authority has a duty to find her somewhere to live because otherwise the children's basic need for shelter would not be met.

Children also need clothes and shoes. Some families can find these expensive, especially as children's feet keep growing and their shoes need replacing frequently. As children get older they often think more about what they are wearing and children from poor homes may feel embarrassed by their clothes.

Food and water

On pages 62–63 we looked at the importance of food and water. They are both essential for our survival and children need them to grow and be healthy.

Love and security

Children need consistent love and care. They need to know that they are liked and valued all of the time and that the people caring for them will not keep changing. This gives children a sense of security and confidence. Some children who do not have consistent love and care can fail to grow and develop as well as other children.

Case Study

Annya is two years old. A neighbour phoned social services because she could hear her sobbing endlessly at night. She was being left alone all night while her mother went out to work. The local authority had a duty to make sure that Annya's needs were being met. A social worker is now working with the mother to make sure that Annya is safe and healthy.

Children's rights

In this country and in many others, there are laws to protect children and to make sure that their basic needs are met. This means that children have rights in law.

Children Act 2004

This law is very important and sets out the rights of children as well as the duties of parents and local authorities. It says that the welfare of the child is paramount. This means that what is best for the child has to be thought about first in any decision being made. The Act also says that children's own views must be listened to. It makes it clear that local authorities must ensure services are provided for children 'in need'.

- Having a **routine**
- Being praised
- Being with the same carers
- **Things that help children feel secure**
- Knowing they are liked
- Knowing that carers are always pleased to see them
- Being able to have toys and comforters
- Knowing they are safe

- Being told off or shouted at
- Being ignored
- Feeling that no one cares for them
- Being with people who are moody
- **Things that make children feel unsettled**
- Feeling they are not liked
- Not knowing or understanding what is happening to them
- Being left with people they don't know very well

▲ This child is having one of her needs met.

United Nations Convention on the Rights of the Child

As well as laws to protect and care for children in this country, there are international laws. In 1991, the United Kingdom agreed to the United Nations Convention on the Rights of the Child.

Activity

Look at these two snippets of conversation.

Adult: If you don't help me clear up, I won't like you any more.

Adult: I was hoping you'd help me tidy up because you're very good at it.

1. Which of these comments will help a child feel confident?
2. Why is it important that all children receive love and care?

Summary

- The basic needs of children are: warmth and shelter; food and water; love and care.
- Adults who work with children must make sure that these needs are being met.
- There are laws to protect children and make sure their needs are being met.

Parents' difficulties in meeting children's needs

The term 'parent' in these pages is also used to mean other people who may be responsible for bringing up a child. This could include foster parents, step-parents or grandparents.

Being a parent is a very hard task, but most parents are able to meet the basic needs of a child. Some parents, however, find it difficult to meet the basic needs of their children.

Difficulty in being a parent

Most parents find they can love and care for their children easily. It seems to come naturally, even though at times they may get cross or feel very tired. Some parents can find it hard to love and care for their children. This may be because their own parents did not love and care for them, so they have not learned the skills. Very young parents can find that they are not ready to take on the responsibility of looking after someone else. They may find it too much for them.

Poverty

Depression and illness

Reasons why parents may not be able to meet their children's basic needs

Difficulty in taking on the parenting role

Alcohol and drug abuse

Depression and illness

Sometimes parents are not able to care for their children because they are too ill themselves. They may have a mental illness which stops them from being able to care. Some mothers can suffer from postnatal depression which stops them from being able to love their children. This can last a few months, but most mothers who get help are eventually able to love and care for their children.

Case study

Sharon was 16 when she gave birth to Sam. She was proud to be a mother and enjoyed the attention. After a few weeks of waking in the night and not being able to go out with her friends, she started to feel 'down'.

Her boyfriend also stopped coming round and then she found out that he was going out with someone else. She started leaving Sam in his cot and going out for an hour or two in the evening. Tonight, she got so cross with his non-stop crying that she stuck a dummy in his mouth and slapped him.

Case study

Sandra is 35 years old and has two other children. She has never suffered from depression and was looking forward to having another baby. Michael was born after a difficult birth and she was surprised that she did not have any particular feelings towards him. This had not happened with the other children. Things got worse after she went home, and for months she was unable to cope. Eventually, she saw her doctor who recognised that she had **postnatal depression**. She began treatment and quickly began to feel better.

Alcohol and drug abuse

Some parents may be addicted to drugs or alcohol. This means that, although they may care for their children, they cannot always meet their needs. Money is spent on drugs or alcohol rather than on food and housing. Drugs and alcohol also change the way people think and act.

Poverty

Children whose parents are poor may not always have all their basic needs met. They may not have shoes that fit or clothes that are warm enough. Although families who have low incomes do get money from the government, it can still be hard for them to make ends meet. Parents who do not have enough money to pay bills often cut down on heating and food. A few become depressed as a result of always being poor and may lose the energy to look after their children properly.

▲ Most parents find that they love and care for their children automatically. A few parents are unable to do so.

Help for children and families

The 2004 Children Act says that all children must have their basic needs met. This may mean that local authorities provide more help for families or that, if a child comes to actual harm, they are taken into 'care'. Taking children away from their parents is only done when a child is likely to be harmed, as the Act makes it clear that the best place for children to be is with their parents. See pages 178–79 to find out what you should do if you think that a child is in danger.

Activity

Read this comment.

'Teenage mothers would be better to give up their babies for adoption as they often can't cope. That way they could start their lives again and their children would have a better chance.'

1   In pairs, discuss what you feel about this comment.

2   Do you think that this person is making a fair point?

Summary

- Most parents are able to meet the basic needs of their children.
- Some parents find it hard to take on the responsibility of being a parent.
- Poverty, depression and addiction are some reasons why children's needs are not met.

Caring for babies' skin, hair, teeth and feet

Keeping babies' skin, hair and teeth clean is important for their health. Germs can build up on our bodies and cause infections. Before changing a nappy or bathing a baby, you must be shown how.

Asking parents

Parents know how best to meet their babies' needs. Some babies may have dry skin which needs oil. Others may have very sensitive skin and need special products. Many babies have a certain time when they are bathed. Before caring for a baby, you must find out how the parents would like you to do so.

Skin

Babies should be kept out of the sun as their skin can easily burn. Sun hats and sun cream may be needed when it is hot. Keeping babies' skin clean prevents infection and keeps them comfortable. There are two ways to wash babies:

- **topping and tailing**
- bathing.

Topping and tailing is washing a baby's face, hands and bottom so these areas stay clean and fresh. Some parents do this with very young babies instead of bathing them daily. Topping and tailing is also done between baths to keep babies comfortable.

Bathing: Most babies are bathed every day, although some parents prefer to run water over them for religious reasons. You must be shown how to bath a baby.

- *Never* leave babies alone in the bath.
- Check that the water temperature is 37°C.
- Have everything to hand.
- Take off any jewellery or watches that might scratch the baby.

Bathing a baby

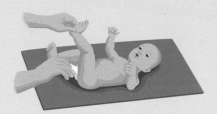

Step 1

Prepare everything you will need first – bath, warm water (not hot), clean clothes, nappy, towels, etc.

Put the baby on a flat surface, undress the baby and take the nappy off.

Clean the nappy area.

Check the temperature of the water (37°C or skin temperature).

Step 2

Wrap the baby gently, but securely, in the towel and wash the face with damp cotton wool.

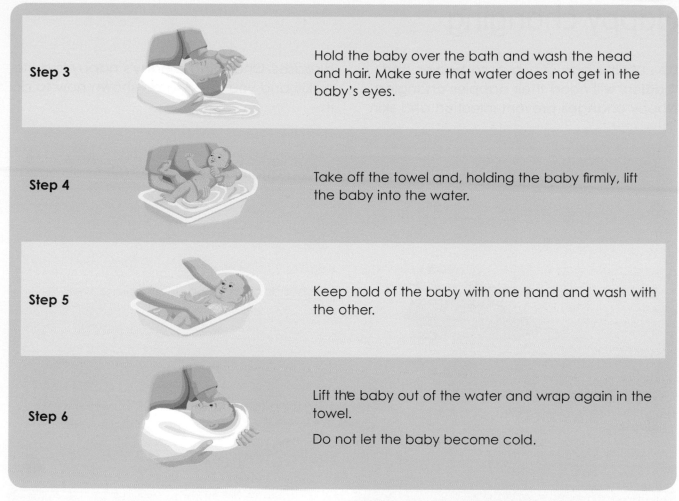

Step 3		Hold the baby over the bath and wash the head and hair. Make sure that water does not get in the baby's eyes.
Step 4		Take off the towel and, holding the baby firmly, lift the baby into the water.
Step 5		Keep hold of the baby with one hand and wash with the other.
Step 6		Lift the baby out of the water and wrap again in the towel. Do not let the baby become cold.

Hair

Babies' hair needs to be gently brushed with a soft brush or wide-toothed comb. If babies have lots of hair, ask parents how they want it to be styled.

Teeth

Many babies start getting their first teeth at six months. These need to be very gently brushed. To stop teeth from decaying, you should not give babies sugary drinks or foods.

Feet

The bones in babies' feet are still forming so they do not wear shoes until they can walk. Socks and babygros must be big enough so feet are not squashed. Toe and hand nails must be cut using baby scissors; take care not to cut the skin. Cut toe nails straight across; hand nails can be gently shaped. This may be easier when the baby is asleep or relaxed.

Activity

Make a list of essential items that you would need to care for babies' skin, hair, teeth and feet.

Summary

- Never leave babies alone in baths.
- Always check the water temperature.
- Change nappies often wearing disposable gloves.
- Do not give babies food and drink with sugar in.
- Babies need plenty of room in socks and babygros for their feet.

Nappy changing

Up until the age of two or so, babies and toddlers will need their nappies changing. Nappy changes prevent infection and skin diseases. Changing a baby's nappy is quite a skill and you need to be shown how to do it.

Step-by-step nappy changing

NB: You must be shown how to do this.

Step 1		Wash your hands and put on disposable gloves.
Step 2	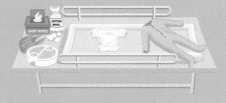	Have everything to hand – cotton wool, water, new nappy, changing mat, bag for dirty nappy, clean clothes.
Step 3		Lay the baby on the mat and undress the baby.
Step 4		Undo the nappy.
Step 5		Gently lift the baby's legs by the ankles.

Step 6 — Wipe off faeces using cotton wool or baby wipes and thoroughly clean the genital area – wipe girls from front to back to avoid infection; do not pull back the foreskin on boys.

Step 7 — Make sure the skin in the nappy area is dry.

Step 8 — Put on a clean nappy.

Nappy changing

Changing babies' nappies is important to prevent infections and nappy rash. Wear disposable gloves and wash your hands before and after.

- Change dirty nappies straightaway.
- Wet nappies must be changed.
- Never use nappies more than once.
- Wash and dry the baby before putting on a new nappy.
- Do not flush nappies down toilets.
- Put nappies in bags and throw away in special bags or bins.
- **Never** leave a baby on a high surface.

Nappy rash is a red 'angry' rash that can appear quickly on babies' bottoms. It can become infected and must be treated.

- Wash and dry the baby's skin very gently but carefully.
- Allow the baby time without a nappy on.
- Change nappies more often.
- Find out if you can put a barrier cream on, such as Vaseline®, once the skin is clean and really dry.

Activity

Answer this reader's letter

> Dear Ann
>
> I'm trying to save money by cutting down on nappy changes and using the same nappy again. The problem is my baby has bad nappy rash. What should I do?
>
> Yours, Sasha

Summary

- Find out from parents about how to care for their child's skin.
- Always wear disposable gloves.
- As a student, you should always be supervised when changing nappies.

Caring for toddlers' skin, hair, teeth and feet

Toddlers are active and can get very dirty. Keeping them clean is important to prevent infections. Many toddlers are also trying to do things for themselves, and adults should encourage this.

Finding out about a toddler's needs from parents

Parents know about their child's skin and hair. This means you must follow their advice and keep their child clean according to their wishes. Some families will want their child to wash their hands under running water and have a shower rather than a bath.

Hands

Toddlers' hands get very dirty. They hold food, touch the floor and use their hands to explore. Toddlers are keen to wash their own hands, but adults must always stay near them in case the water is too hot or they miss bits. Toddlers may need a plastic step to reach the washbasin and may need reminding to dry their hands.

Nails must be trimmed and should be shaped. This is best done after their hands have been washed, when they will be relaxed. You could make a game of it, such as 'This little piggy went to market'.

Faces and noses

Toddlers need to have their faces washed during the day; especially after eating. It is also important to make sure toddlers' noses are wiped to prevent infections. Most toddlers do not like having their faces and noses wiped so it is a good idea to encourage them to do it themselves. You could make a game of it or give them a teddy to pretend on.

Nappy changing

Many toddlers are in nappies until they are two, or even three, years old. Do not leave them in a dirty nappy, as they quickly develop nappy rash. Some toddlers do not want their nappy changed and you may need to give them a toy or book to hold. It is a good idea to praise toddlers and talk to them so they stay still. When changing toddlers' nappies, do not:

- leave the dirty nappy, wipes, etc. near them, as they may touch them
- leave any cream or baby wipes where they can reach them.

Moving out of nappies

At some time during the second or third year, toddlers will want to move out of nappies. There are some signs that they are ready to leave nappies:

- pulling at a nappy when dirty
- nappies are dry for longer
- interest in toilets or potties.

It is important not to rush toddlers or make them feel they have failed if they have accidents. Adults can help toddlers who are 'toilet training' by making sure there are potties nearby and that toddlers' clothes are easy to remove.

Adults must stay close to toddlers when they are washing their hands.

Skin

Like babies, toddlers should not be exposed to strong sunlight as their skin will easily burn. They should be protected by hats, T-shirts and high-factor sun cream.

Most toddlers need a bath or shower each day. They get very dirty and food tends to appear in interesting places! Most toddlers love being in the bath or shower and want to play with toys. Many adults wash toddlers with a flannel while they are playing and it is a good time to sing some songs and chat. When bathing toddlers:

- **never** leave them alone
- make sure the water is warm, but not too hot
- have clean clothes and towels ready
- encourage them to play.

Hair

Toddlers' hair needs washing quite often because it gets dirty with food and other things. It is normally washed at bath or shower time. Many toddlers dislike having their hair washed. They are frightened of getting water in their eyes. This means that only a little gentle shampoo should be used and toddlers should be encouraged to do as much as they can themselves. It is also a good idea to have plenty of towels for wiping faces.

Toddlers' hair is starting to grow and needs brushing or combing, depending on hair type. Some toddlers dislike having their hair touched so it is a good idea to pretend to do it to a doll and encourage the child to pretend as well.

Teeth

Most toddlers have quite a few of their teeth and are very proud of them. Their teeth need cleaning at least twice a day after meals. Avoid sugary foods and drinks. Most toddlers want to brush their own teeth. This is fine, but an adult will also need to do them because most toddlers suck or bite their toothbrushes.

Feet

Toddlers' feet are growing so it is important that their shoes and socks fit them. Indoors, it is good to let them be barefoot or in socks, as long as the floor is not slippery. This allows the feet to spread and develop. Toe nails should be cut straight across – not shaped. It is easier to cut nails after a child has been in the bath as the water makes the nails softer.

- Look out for shoes and socks that are too small.
- Make sure shoes are not too big or are slipping off the foot.
- Make sure shoes are fastened securely to prevent the foot from slipping.

Activity

Can you answer this reader's letter?

> My toddler has a runny nose. Every time I try to wipe it she turns her head and runs away. Sometimes I just decide to leave it. She has recently had an ear infection and the doctor says I must keep cleaning her nose. Any ideas?

Summary

- Many toddlers get themselves dirty.
- Toddlers want to do many things for themselves.
- Toddlers often dislike having their faces and hair washed.
- Toddlers may need to be distracted while having their nappies changed.

Caring for pre-school children

As children get older, it is important that they learn how to take care of themselves, but pre-school children will need some encouragement and help.

It is still important to find out from children's parents whether children have any special requirements. They may have skin conditions such as eczema, or they may need to wash using only running water. As children get older, they will be able to tell us themselves what their needs are.

Pre-school children

Toileting

Most pre-school children will be able to use the toilet themselves. They may need some help to undress, but otherwise will be quite independent. Sometimes they may leave it a little late and have an accident!

- Make sure children wash their hands after using the toilet.
- Girls should wipe themselves from front to back.
- Handle any accidents in a matter-of-fact way and do not get angry with the child.
- Always wear disposable gloves when cleaning up any accidents.

Teeth

Children should be encouraged to clean their own teeth, although an adult should 'finish off' the job. Begin to talk about why brushing teeth is so important and encourage children to look at their teeth in the mirror.

Skin

All children should be kept out of the strong sun and T-shirts and hats should be worn. High-factor sun cream should also be applied to prevent damage to the skin.

Most pre-school children love bath and shower time and are happier about hair washing as long as they are involved. They can wash themselves with some help. They should never be left alone. It is important that their skin is dried carefully so that it does not chap and become sore.

Hands and noses

It is essential that children wash their hands because of the risk of infection. Adults also need to trim children's nails. These should be cut and shaped to the finger.

To stop cross-infection and prevent children from getting ear infections, it is important that they blow their noses. Adults may need to help them by holding the tissue and encouraging them to blow.

- Praise children when they remember to wash their hands.
- Check that hands are washed before eating and after using the toilet.
- Make sure children's noses are clean.
- Throw away tissues after they have been used.

Feet

Children's feet are still growing and shoes and socks must be a good fit. Socks should also be worn with shoes to prevent the foot rubbing against the shoes, which might cause blisters. Children's feet may need to be checked for athlete's foot, a fungal infection that makes the skin peel, and also for verrucas, which are like warts.

Hair

Hair will need brushing or combing. It is also important to check for head lice as they are quite common in this age group. Look out for small white nits that look like dandruff but do not move.

- Look out for head lice.
- Encourage children to brush their own hair.

Activity

Observe how staff can help children to become independent.

Write about one of the ways that you have seen.

Summary

- Allow pre-school children opportunities to become independent.
- Check children's hair for head lice.
- Talk to pre-school children about why personal hygiene is important.

Caring for school children

Even when children are older, it is still important to take care of their skin, hair, teeth and feet. School children will want to do most of their skin, hair and teeth care for themselves. It is also important that they are praised so they feel good and enjoy looking after themselves.

Privacy

As children get older, it is important that they are given some privacy – for example, they may shut the door when using the toilet or they may want to change in private.

Reminders and praise

There will be times when children forget to wash their hands or do not clean their teeth. It is important to give reminders and also to praise children when they have taken the time to look after themselves properly. Many settings will put up signs to help children remember.

▲ This child is starting to care for herself.

School children	
Skin care	● Children can wash themselves, although adults should still be around. ● Adults need to trim nails. ● Make sure children spend time drying themselves properly. ● Children should not be exposed to the sun in the summer. If outdoors, high-factor sun cream should be used.
Hair	● Check for head lice every day. ● Encourage children to brush or comb their hair.
Toileting	● Occasional accidents may still occur. Do not get angry; just reassure the child. ● Make sure hands are washed afterwards.
Teeth	● Teeth need cleaning after meals. ● Make sure children know how to clean their teeth properly. ● Do not give children sugary drinks or foods.
Feet	● Adults need to trim toe nails. ● Look out for infections such as athlete's foot and verrucas. ● Check that shoes are the right size.

Health topics

If children understand why looking after their bodies is important they are more likely to want to do so. Topics about hands, teeth and skin can all help children to learn about keeping healthy. Adults can also talk to children as they are doing things like cleaning their teeth.

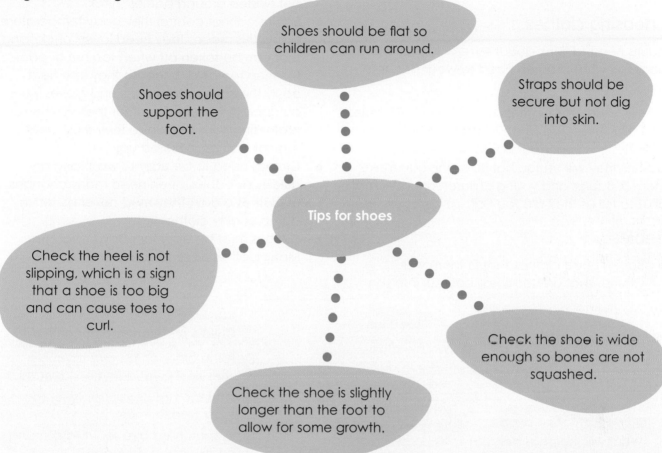

Shoes should be flat so children can run around.

Shoes should support the foot.

Straps should be secure but not dig into skin.

Tips for shoes

Check the heel is not slipping, which is a sign that a shoe is too big and can cause toes to curl.

Check the shoe is wide enough so bones are not squashed.

Check the shoe is slightly longer than the foot to allow for some growth.

Summary

- Pre-school children and school children are becoming more independent.
- Adults need to praise and remind children about washing hands, cleaning teeth, etc.
- Check children's hair for head lice.
- Health topics can help children understand why good hygiene is important.

Activity

Make a sign that will help school children remember to wash their hands.

Why is it important to put signs up?

Choosing clothes for babies and children

Adults working with children need to choose appropriate clothing and footwear for them. Look at pages 119, 121 and 123 for information about footwear.

Choosing clothes

Adults need to think about several factors when deciding what children need to wear (see the diagram below).

Ideally, children's clothes should be comfortable and allow the child to easily take part in activities. It is important not to dress children in clothes they will be too hot in, as this can make them ill. Babies and young children are often not able to tell us they are too hot.

Babies

- Babies need clothes that fit them well. Clothes that are too small can cut into skin and damage feet. Clothes that are too large can be dangerous, as sleeves and legs can get twisted up. Home-made clothes must be checked for safety – for example, ribbons can get twisted around babies' neck.

- Babies cannot control their body temperature easily. This means they need layers of clothing that can be taken off when too hot or added to when too cold. Because they lose heat easily they need warm hats and gloves when outdoors in winter. In summer their skin needs protecting from the sun so they must wear a sun hat and be covered up.

- Clothes need to be easy to wash and dry quickly as babies often need many changes of clothes a day. They must never be left in damp or dirty clothes.

- Clothes must be easy for nappy changes. Many clothes have poppers.

Location
- Will the child be outdoors or indoors?
- What will the temperature be?

Child's preference and comfort
- Does an older child have favourite clothes that give them confidence?
- Are the clothes comfortable for the child to wear?
- Does the child have sensitive skin and need all-cotton garments?

Activity
- What will the child be doing, e.g. crawling, painting, climbing?
- Will the clothes be suitable or will they be a nuisance?

Things to think about when choosing clothes

Weather
- Is it going to be hot, cold, sunny or windy?
- Will the child be warm enough or too hot?

Stage of development of the child
- Is the child able to dress and undress themselves?
- Are the clothes easy to remove for nappy changing?
- Will the clothes allow a baby to crawl easily?

Ease of care
- Are the clothes easy to wash and care for?
- Will the clothes stain or be difficult to clean?

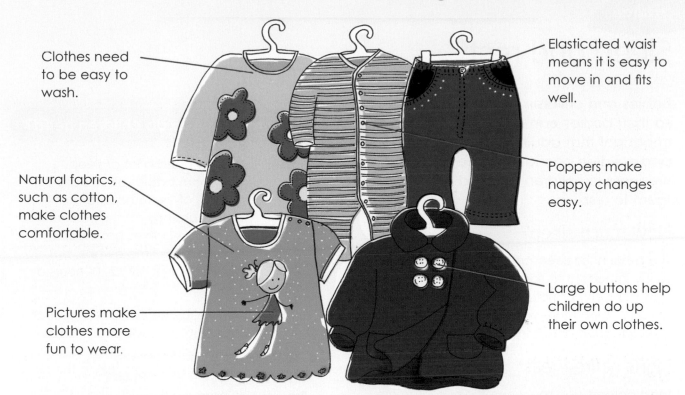

Clothes need to be easy to wash.

Natural fabrics, such as cotton, make clothes comfortable.

Pictures make clothes more fun to wear.

Elasticated waist means it is easy to move in and fits well.

Poppers make nappy changes easy.

Large buttons help children do up their own clothes.

Toddlers

- Clothes must be a good fit so toddlers can move easily.
- Clothes must be easily taken off for nappy changes and potty training.
- Clothes must be strong enough to cope with the wear and tear of an active toddler.
- Clothes need to be easy to wash and dry as they may need one or two changes.
- Toddlers need to wear sun hats as their skin is sensitive. They should also be covered up with T-shirts in the summer.
- Toddlers may need bibs to help keep their clothes clean.

Pre-school and school children

- Clothes need to be easy for children to dress themselves.
- Clothes need to be comfortable and easy to care for.
- Clothes need to be suitable for playing in, outside and inside.
- Children may also need aprons for some activities.
- Children will need a change of underwear every day to prevent infection.

Activity

In pairs work out what clothes and footwear these children will need:

1 School children playing outdoors in the snow.
2 A toddler eating his dinner indoors at home on a hot day.
3 A baby out in a pram on a wet and windy day in February.
4 A pre-school child who is in indoors in a nursery in May.

Summary

- When choosing clothes, think about the weather and the temperature.
- When it is sunny and hot, children need to wear sun hats and to be covered up.
- Clothes must be appropriate for the stage of development of the child and the activities they are doing.
- Babies and toddlers need several changes of clothes.

Sleep and rest

Babies and children need rest and sleep so their bodies can grow and develop. It is important that adults who work with babies and children can identify the signs of tiredness in children and find ways to help them to rest.

How much sleep?

The amount of sleep can vary from child to child, so it is important to find out from parents when their children normally sleep. Many babies and children sleep more when they are going through a **growth spurt** or fighting off an illness.

Signs of tiredness

Most parents can see when their children are tired, because they know them well. Babies tend to have their own 'tired' cry, while toddlers' and older children's behaviour and appearance may give us clues that they need to sleep.

How much sleep do children need?	
Babies	Babies need a lot of sleep. Newborn babies often sleep for a total of 14–15 hours a day, although they do this in several sleeps. As babies get older they spend more time awake, but they still sleep for 12–14 hours a day.
Toddlers	Most toddlers can sleep through the night and will often need 11–12 hours' sleep. Most will also need a short nap during the day.
Pre-school and school children	Children will need a good night's sleep and some pre-school children also enjoy a short afternoon nap. Adults also need to make sure children have plenty of opportunities to rest.

▲ Look out for the signs of tiredness.

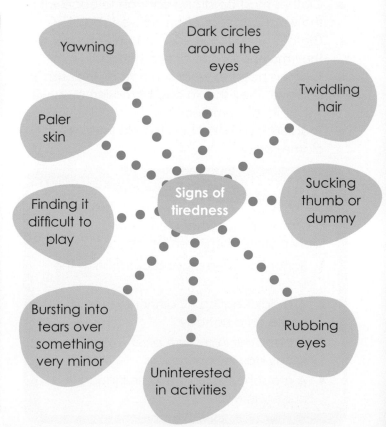

- Yawning
- Dark circles around the eyes
- Twiddling hair
- Paler skin
- Finding it difficult to play
- **Signs of tiredness**
- Sucking thumb or dummy
- Bursting into tears over something very minor
- Uninterested in activities
- Rubbing eyes

Putting babies to sleep safely

To help prevent **cot death**, it is important that babies are put down to sleep following these guidelines.

- Place babies on their backs to sleep, towards the bottom of the cot.
- Do not let babies become too hot – use blankets not duvets.
- Make sure that blankets do not cover the baby's face.
- Check the room temperature – it should be around 18°C.
- Do not use pillows or cot bumpers.
- Remove cuddly toys – they might smother the baby.
- Never smoke in a baby's room or near the baby.
- Never leave a baby alone with a bottle in case they choke.
- It is also important to check on the baby when they are sleeping.

Putting toddlers to sleep

Many toddlers fight sleep. It is useful if there is a routine so they learn about going to sleep.

Most toddlers and children need to relax and unwind before they can get to sleep. Most parents bathe their toddlers as part of the bedtime routine to help them relax. Many group care settings do not leave toddlers until they have fallen asleep. It is important to check the sleeping area for safety, as toddlers may get out of bed and start exploring!

Activity

Harry's mum says it is difficult to get him to sleep at night. He is four years old and after tea he always has a bath followed by a game of 'rough and tumble' with his parents. He is then put into bed.

1 In pairs, work out why Harry might find it difficult to get to sleep.

2 What advice could you give his parents?

Helping children to rest

Some children may not need to sleep but still need to rest in the afternoon or after tiring physical activity. Resting helps the body and mind to relax. This is important so children don't get overtired. It is also important to create an atmosphere that is quiet and calm. Children will find it hard to rest if they are hungry or thirsty.

Looking at books

Giving children shapes or objects to sort

Reading a story

Putting on soft music

Activities that can help children rest

Easy jigsaw puzzles

Listening to a story CD or watching a video

Helping toddlers to nap

- Make sure the toddler is not hungry or thirsty.
  Change nappy or take to toilet.
- Plan some quiet activities.
  Take off outer clothing and shoes.
- Give toddler comforter or favourite cuddly toy.
  Check the room is safe.
- Take toddler to quiet area or bed and read story.

Summary

- Sleep is needed to keep healthy.
- Babies and toddlers need to sleep more than older children.
- Babies must be put to sleep on their backs and must not get too hot.
- Rooms must be checked for safety.
- Routines help toddlers and children know it is time to rest or sleep.

Daily routines

A daily routine is the pattern of a day. A good routine helps children's growth and development because it meets their basic needs. It also helps children feel secure, as they know that similar things happen each day.

Planning a daily routine

Routines change according to the age of children. This means that adults planning a daily routine need to think about the needs of the children they are working with.

Need	Why	You should check:
Food and water	Babies need to be fed more often than older children. Toddlers and young children need snacks and drinks as well as main meals. Children need to have a balanced diet in order to be healthy (see pages 62–63).	<ul><li>how often children need feeding</li><li>what times of the day they drink and eat.</li></ul>
Fresh air and exercise	Fresh air is important as it helps children build up an appetite and can help prevent infection. Exercise is also needed, as it helps children's muscles and bones to develop.	<ul><li>when it is possible to go outside</li><li>what equipment, if any, is needed.</li></ul>
Rest and sleep	Rest and sleep help children's bodies to grow and also stop them from becoming overtired.	<ul><li>how much rest and sleep the child needs</li><li>when the child normally rests and sleeps.</li></ul>
Love and security	Children need routines. They also need 'quality' time with adults, when they can build up a relationship. Story time or playing alone with one or two children can help them to feel secure.	<ul><li>at what points in the day children can have some individual or quality time with an adult.</li></ul>
Stimulation	Babies and children need to have time to play and be active. Toys, equipment and activities need to be offered for all ages.	<ul><li>what times in the day children are lively and ready to play.</li></ul>
Physical care	Keeping the skin, hair and teeth clean is important to keep babies and children healthy. Babies also need to have their nappies changed often.	<ul><li>when hands will need washing</li><li>when children will need to go to the toilet and/or wash their hands</li><li>at what point babies will need their nappies changed (in addition to when they are dirty)</li><li>at what time children have their baths or showers.</li></ul>

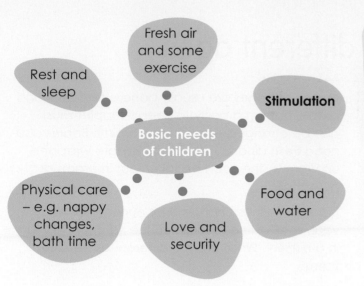

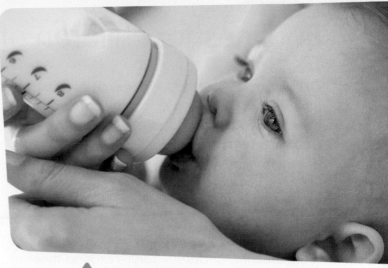

△ What basic needs are being met here?

Morning care routine for a two-year-old at home

	Time	Activity	
	7.00am	Wake and cuddle with parents	Love and security
		Nappy change	Physical care
Food and drink	7.30am	Breakfast	
Physical care	8.00am	Face and hands washed	
		Dressed	
		Hair brushed	
	8.30am	Play with toys	Stimulation
Physical care	9.30am	Nappy change	
Fresh air and exercise		Trip outdoors to feed ducks	
		Roll and kick ball	
	10.30am	Wash hands	Physical care
		Drink of milk and fruit	Food and drink
Physical care	10.45am	Nappy check	
Rest and sleep, love and security		Story, cuddle and nap	
	11.45am	Nappy change	Physical care
		Play with dough	Stimulation
Physical care	12.15pm	Wash hands	
Food and water		Lunch	

Activity

Adults also have routines! In pairs, work out the routine of a typical day in your life.

1 How much sleep and rest do you need?

2 How much exercise and fresh air do you get?

3 How much time do you spend playing or having fun in some way?

Summary

- A daily routine is the pattern of a day.
- Routines help children stay healthy by meeting their basic needs.
- Routines help children feel secure.
- Routines change according to the needs of children.

Routines for children of different ages

On pages 128–29 we looked at the factors involved in planning a routine for children. It is also important to see how routines vary according to the ages of children.

Routines for babies

Most parents find that it is the baby who sets the routine rather than the parents! This is because babies will cry if they are not having their needs met. Routines for babies centre around their need for regular feeds and sleep.

Nappy changes are usually done after feeds and before putting a baby to sleep. Nappies must also be changed when they are dirty. Babies also need fresh air and, provided they are wrapped up warmly, they can be taken out in prams or pushchairs.

Babies' routines change a lot during their first year. Look at the routines on the right for babies in a nursery. What are the differences between them?

Routine at 3 months	🕐
7.30am	Arrive and settle in
8.00am	Bottle
8.40am	Nappy change, nap
10.00am	Nappy change
10.15am	Play
10.30am	Walk in a pushchair
11.00am	Wash hands, play
12.00pm	Bottle, wash hands and face
12.45pm	Nappy change, nap
2.45pm	Nappy change
3.15pm	Play and rhymes
4.00pm	Bottle
4.40pm	Nappy change, play
5.00pm	Home

Routine at 8 months	🕐
7.30am	Arrive and settle in
8.00am	Breakfast
8.30am	Nappy change
8.45am	Play
10.00am	Wash hands, drink and snack
10.15am	Rhymes and show books
10.30am	Walk in a pushchair
11.00am	Wash hands, nappy change and nap
12.00pm	Lunch, wash hands and face
12.30pm	Play
12.45pm	Nappy change
1.00pm	Play with water, wash hands
2.30pm	Nappy change, nap
3.00pm	Snack and drink
3.15pm	Play and rhymes
4.30pm	Tea and nappy change
5.00pm	Home

Routines for toddlers

Routines for toddlers will vary depending on whether they are being cared for at home or in a nursery. They will still need to have their needs met – for example, nap time and time to play. Routines in homes may have to be adapted if there are also other children or a baby to be looked after.

Home routine for Curran, aged 2 years, 3 months	
7.00am	Wake up, nappy change, breakfast
8.00am	Washed, dressed and hair combed
8.30am	Play with toys indoors
9.00am	Check nappy, walk to parent and toddler group
9.15am	Play at parent and toddler group
10.30am	Juice and biscuit at toddler group
10.45am	Nappy change
11.30am	Leave toddler group and walk home
12.00pm	Wash hands, lunch
12.45pm	Story, cuddle, nappy change
1.00pm	Nap
2.30pm	Drink of milk, cuddle and play
2.50pm	Nappy check
3.00pm	Walk to play area
3.45pm	Return home, wash hands, piece of fruit
5.00pm	Tea
5.30pm	Bath time
6.00pm	Story and bed

Routines for pre-school children

Many pre-school children go to nursery, play group or pre-school. They may spend quite a lot of their time there and so it is important that the setting's routine can meet the children's basic needs.

Routine of the morning – Clive Area Nursery	
9.00am	Welcome to the nursery – free play
9.50am	Group time and introduction to activities
10.00am	Free play and planned activities
10.30am	Milk and snack bar opens – hands have to be washed
11.00am	Outdoor play
11.45am	Wash hands
11.50am	Story time and rhymes
12.00pm	Goodbye song and home time

(Children go to the toilet and wash hands when they want, accompanied by an adult.)

Activity

Look at the routine of the Clive Area Nursery above.

How does it meet the basic needs of pre-school children?

Summary

- Routines of babies and children change according to their needs.
- Routines must meet the basic needs of children.

End of unit summary

Clothing and footwear

- Work out what type of clothes they will need for warm weather.
- How will you make sure they are comfortable?
- Why will it be important for them to wear sun hats if they are outside?

Hair, skin and teeth

- When will they need to clean their teeth?
- When will they need to wash their hands?
- How many nappy changes might the baby need?
- What sort of help will the four-year-old need to wash? How will you care for their hair?

Exercise and stimulation

- How might the baby get some fresh air and exercise?
- How could the four-year-old get some exercise?
- What type of things might a four-year-old enjoy doing? (See also Unit 6.)
- Why is it important for children to be stimulated?

Rest and sleep

- How much sleep would a baby of eight months need?
- When might the four-year-old go to bed?
- What signs might the four-year-old show when he or she is tired?

Meal times

- When will the four-year-old need to be fed and have snacks?
- When will the baby need feeding?

End of unit task: Children's needs

You have been asked to help look after two children aged eight months and four years for the day, from breakfast time through to bedtime. The weather is likely to be quite warm and sunny. In pairs:

- work out what the care needs are for each of the children
- use the boxes below to help you think about their different needs
- plan a routine for the day showing how the children's needs might be met.

Back to the real world

You should now understand why routines are important when caring for children. You should also have an understanding of how to meet the basic needs of children.

1 Can you make a list of the basic needs of children?

2 Can you give two reasons why some parents may have difficulty in meeting their children's needs?

3 Can you explain why it is important that children have a routine?

Glossary

cot death When a baby dies suddenly while asleep

postnatal depression Depression that some mothers feel after giving birth

routine Repeated pattern or order to a day or period of time

shelter Somewhere to live

stimulation Activities to make the brain active

topping and tailing Washing a baby's face, hands and bottom

My story

Amelia

I work in a children's centre. We have children that come in from six months through until they go to school. It is interesting to see the differences between the babies and toddlers and the older children. With our little ones, we have to be very organised and make sure that we stick to a routine. It is easier with older children as they are able to tell us if they are hungry or tired. Older children are also easier to care for as they tend to dress themselves and know when they need the toilet, although you have to allow enough time. Three-year-olds are not speedy dressers!

Unit 6 Play and practical activities

All babies and children love to play – and so do many adults. Play is an important way for children to learn. There are many different types of play and children gain different skills from different types of play. Adults need to provide a range of play opportunities for children. This might mean putting out equipment or it might mean playing with children.

This unit will help you find out about the importance of different types of play. You will also learn how to set up and present play activities and how adults can support children's play. This unit covers the following:

- the importance of play as part of learning and development
- types of play and leisure activities for children
- how play and learning activities are selected and prepared
- the role of the adult in supporting children's play.

The topics you will find in this unit are:

- How play helps learning (1 and 2)
- How play helps physical development
- Play and social and emotional needs
- Recognising children's different play needs
- Indoor and outdoor physical play
- Creative play
- Imaginative play
- Sand and water play
- Construction play, block play and social play
- Stories and rhymes
- Music
- Setting up for play and activities
- Selecting activities and resources
- Planning and reviewing play and activities
- The role of the adult in supporting play and learning
- Choosing equipment

In the real world

You are on placement and your supervisor asks you to plan some activities to promote the physical skills of children aged three years. She also asks you to think about how you might do some of the activities outdoors. Finally, she says that you should observe the children and plan other activities based on what you have seen. You are worried because you are not sure what type of equipment or activities would work with this age group. You are also not sure about how to observe children or to plan further.

By the end of this unit you should have an understanding of the play needs of different ages of children and the importance of observing them as they play.

How play helps learning (1)

All children, even babies, enjoy playing. Why children play is not completely understood, but it is known that children learn through play. It is now considered that early years settings, including schools, now have to use play to help children learn. (You may ask your tutor if you can look at the Early Years Foundation Stage, if you live in England, or the Foundation Stage, if you live in Wales.)

Look at some of the things a four-year-old might learn by playing and sharing LEGO® with another child:

space

how things are put together

what happens when things fall

shape

Playing with LEGO® helps children learn about:

how to use their hands and eyes

colours

how to concentrate

how to play with other children

As well as helping children to learn, play helps children in each of the areas of development.

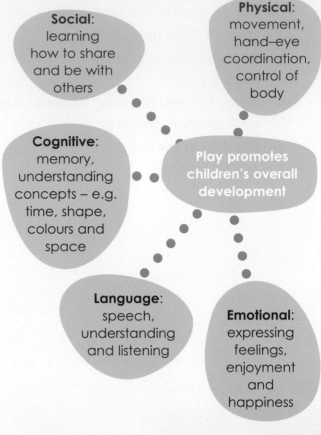

Social: learning how to share and be with others

Physical: movement, hand–eye coordination, control of body

Cognitive: memory, understanding concepts – e.g. time, shape, colours and space

Play promotes children's overall development

Language: speech, understanding and listening

Emotional: expressing feelings, enjoyment and happiness

▲ What skills is this child learning?

Children of different ages play in different ways

The way in which children play changes as they get older and as they develop new skills. Each stage of play is important as it helps children develop.

Babies: The way babies and toddlers play is sometimes called **mastery play**. They repeat movements over and over again as if they are practising. This type of play helps them to control their bodies and movements. They are also finding out about what happens when they touch or move things.

This baby has learned how to make the mobile move.

Case study

An 11-month-old baby sits in his high chair and drops his spoon on the floor. His carer picks it up. He then drops it again and smiles. Each time it is picked up, he drops it again.

Toddlers are mobile and are keen to touch and explore their environment. They also use mastery play and will repeat things over and over again. Toddlers begin to watch the way other children play, although they will not actually play with them. This is sometimes called **spectator play** or **parallel play**. Toddlers also copy what they see and bring this into their play.

Case study

A two-year-old holds a doll by the arm. He puts it in the pram and covers the doll with a blanket. He pushes the pram along and then takes the doll and drops it on the floor. He then picks up the doll and puts it back in the pram again.

Activity

Choose three toys that you think would help a baby to learn.

Explain what you think they will teach the baby.

Summary

- Babies and toddlers learn through play.
- Play changes as they grow.

How play helps learning (2)

We have seen how play helps babies and toddlers to learn. Pre-school and school children also enjoy playing and learning.

Pre-school children often play in a **symbolic** way. This means they make one thing stand for another. They may pretend a stick is a spoon or a piece of dough is cake. Pre-school children also play with toys and equipment that help them learn concepts such as heavy and light or their colours. Sometimes pre-school children also play with each other. This is called **cooperative play**.

School children carry on learning through play. They practise skills they have learned and put knowledge into their play situations. They may, for example, be shown how to make a plane out of paper and later make one to play with themselves. They can also understand why some games need rules and enjoy making up games with rules.

Rules are important as they show that children are trying to work out why things are the way they are.

Case study

Rahima is playing outdoors with Simon. They are mixing grass and leaves together in a bucket.

'We're making a meal and we're going to find more food now,' Rahima says.

Rahima and Simon play this game for about 20 minutes before deciding to play on the tricycles.

▲ Children enjoy playing games with rules.

Case study

Anna is playing with some LEGO®. She is trying to make a house using only yellow bricks. This is her rule for this game. She tells her friend, who is starting to build her own house, that she cannot use any of her yellow bricks because she started using them first. She then adds, 'You can borrow my yellow bricks, but you must ask before taking them.'

This shows Anna has learned a 'rule': that people must ask before borrowing things.

▲ What is this child learning as he plays?

Activity

Adults often carry on playing, but may not realise it. Do you do any of these things?

- Sports
- Board games
- Card games
- Doodling on pads

1   Can you think of any other ways in which adults play?

2   In pairs, talk about why some adults may not admit to 'playing'?

Summary

- All babies and children play.
- Play helps children learn.
- Children's play changes as they get older.

How play helps physical development

While babies and children play, they practise movements and skills. Look at the skills that babies and children need to develop.

Babies

Babies need to learn how to control their bodies. This is a slow process but, by the age of six months, they are able to grasp hold of a small toy and by 12 months, most babies crawl or even walk.

Play helps babies' physical development because they keep practising movements they enjoy. For example, they may grasp hold of a rattle because they like its colour or the sound it makes.

0–6 months: Babies have to learn how to control their **limbs**. Play encourages movement and, by practising movements, babies start to gain control.

6–12 months: During this period, babies become mobile and start exploring.

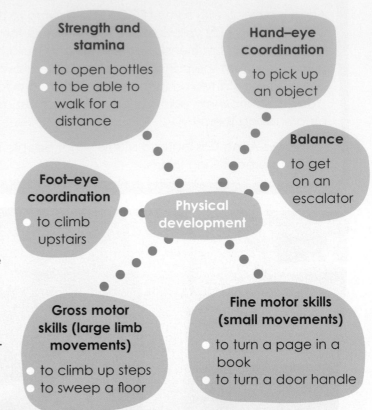

Strength and stamina
- to open bottles
- to be able to walk for a distance

Hand–eye coordination
- to pick up an object

Balance
- to get on an escalator

Foot–eye coordination
- to climb upstairs

Physical development

Gross motor skills (large limb movements)
- to climb up steps
- to sweep a floor

Fine motor skills (small movements)
- to turn a page in a book
- to turn a door handle

Age	Motor skills and coordination	Role of adult
0–6 months	**Fine motor skills and hand–eye coordination** Rattles; mobiles; squeaky toys **Gross motor skills and foot–eye coordination** Baby gym; play music – young babies try to dance on their backs!	Ensure toys are suitable for baby – check instructions; ensure toys are cleaned often as babies will put things in their mouth; do not leave the baby alone; praise the baby; show and put toys in babies' hands.
6–12 months	**Fine motor skills and hand–eye coordination** Pop-up toys; stacking beakers; musical toys; activity mats and centres; posting boxes **Gross motor skills and foot–eye coordination** Music to move to; trolleys with bricks	Do not leave alone; check toys and equipment are safe for this age and are clean; ensure there is enough floor space and it is clean; praise babies; show babies toys; help babies do things – e.g. build a stack of bricks for them to knock down.
Toddlers	**Fine motor skills and hand–eye coordination** Dough; push-along toys; large bricks; shape sorters; stacking beakers; pop-up toys **Gross motor skills and foot–eye coordination** Tricycles and sit-and-ride toys; slide; prams; large soft balls; bean bags	Good supervision; check equipment is suitable for toddlers; check equipment is safe and clean; be patient; give a little help if needed; praise toddlers.

Age	Motor skills and coordination	Role of adult
Pre-school children	**Fine motor skills and hand–eye coordination** Sand and water play; DUPLO® and other construction toys – e.g. train sets, crayons, paints and scissors; dressing-up clothes, jigsaw puzzles; cooking **Gross motor skills and foot–eye coordination** Tricycles and bicycles with stabilisers; large equipment – e.g. slides, benches; balls, bean bags and hoops; play tunnels; obstacle courses; swimming	Supervision; check equipment is clean and safe; ensure children do not become overexcited; put out enough equipment so children can play together; praise children; help children with skills like throwing and catching; encourage children to do everyday tasks – e.g. pouring their own drinks; allow children enough time to play.
School children	**Fine motor skills and hand–eye coordination** Painting and drawing materials; sewing; weaving; modelling materials – e.g. clay, dough; junk modelling; cooking **Gross motor skills and foot–eye coordination** Bicycles, roller skates, skateboards; football, netball and dancing; skipping with ropes; swimming; obstacle courses; large apparatus – e.g. swings, benches, slides, climbing frames	Keep an eye on play and make sure it is safe; check equipment is safe; show children new skills; encourage children to do things for themselves; provide interesting activities; praise children; allow children enough time to play.

At nine months many babies can sit up and reach out to get a toy. They can take a toy from hand to hand and drop it when they have finished with it.

Toddlers

Toddlers are mobile and keen to do things for themselves. Most two-year-olds can build a tower of six blocks and push themselves along on a sit-and-ride toy. By three years old, they can draw a person and pedal and steer a tricycle. Toddlers can become frustrated as they may know exactly what they want to do, but do not yet have the skills to do it.

Pre-school children

Children are starting to play together and be independent. Their skills are still developing, but they may lack strength and coordination. By five years, most children can draw a recognisable picture, use scissors well and catch a soft ball.

School children

School children enjoy using the skills they have developed and are keen to play with other children. Children will use their fine motor skills and hand–eye coordination to help them write and do other activities like making models.

Activity

Choose three toys or activities that would help a four-year-old develop their physical skills.

Explain the reason behind each of your choices. (You might be able to look in a toy catalogue for some more ideas.)

Summary

- Play helps babies and children to practise and gain physical skills.
- Adults must make sure toys and equipment are safe.

Play and social and emotional needs

Babies and children need to learn how to share, play and build relationships. They need to learn how to express their feelings and control their behaviour. Play helps babies and children meet these needs.

Stages of social play

Babies and children gradually learn to play with each other. This is important because, by playing with other children, they learn how to build relationships. At first babies tend only to be able to play with an adult but, by the age of three or four, most children can play with each other.

How play can help children's emotional development

By playing children can learn to express their feelings and this helps them to control their behaviour.

Babies enjoy looking at themselves in a mirror. At first they think they are looking at another baby, but gradually they learn that they are looking at themselves. Babies also learn to share toys if adults offer them toys. By playing with an adult, babies learn to smile and look at other people's reactions and faces.

Toddlers can feel very frustrated because they often want to do things but they can't quite manage them. They also do not understand why they cannot have things. Play helps toddlers feel more in control and they can gain satisfaction from being able to do things themselves.

Toys such as drums and hammer and pegs are good because toddlers can explore feelings of anger and aggression. Toys such as dolls, prams and teddies can encourage feelings of love and caring.

▲ What type of social play are these children showing?

Type of social play	What does this mean?
Solitary play	Up until about two years children usually play alone. They may play with adults, but cannot play with other children. Older children might choose to play alone – e.g. when painting.
Parallel play	From about two years, toddlers start to notice what other children are doing. Parallel play is when children play happily side by side.
Associative play	From about the age of three, children may look to see what other children are doing and copy them. This type of play is sometimes called spectator play because the child is watching.
Cooperative play	Between three and four years, children begin to develop friendships and are able to play together. As they get older they start to be able to organise their play. They may say things like 'let's be puppies'.

Pre-school children are beginning to use language to explain what they want. They are also beginning to play cooperatively. Dressing up and pretending can help children try out different roles. They may copy actions and words they have seen adults and older children do and use. This type of play is sometimes called **role play**.

School children can play together and often act out some of their fears. For example, they might pretend they are lost or all alone. Play also helps school children get a feeling of what it might be like to be someone else.

Ways of helping children's social development

Babies and toddlers

- Understand that babies and toddlers cannot share toys.
- Show babies and toddlers how to share by offering them toys.
- Play peek-a-boo and pat-a-cake with babies to show them how to join in.
- Teach toddlers rhymes so they can join in and share.
- Play with toddlers so they learn the skills of playing.

Pre-school children

- Play board games with pre-school children so they learn how to take turns.
- Make sure there are enough toys and equipment so children don't need to snatch.

School children

- Praise older children when they play and share.

Toddlers love to knock things down. What type of feelings does this allow children to express?

Activities to help children express their feelings

Young children can have very powerful feelings. They do not always have the language skills to talk about how they are feeling. Some activities can help young children to express their feelings.

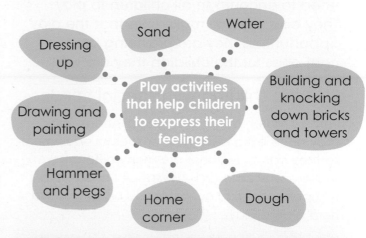

Dressing up • Sand • Water • Drawing and painting • **Play activities that help children to express their feelings** • Building and knocking down bricks and towers • Hammer and pegs • Home corner • Dough

Activity

Can you answer this reader's letter?

Dear Marjorie,
I am worried about my toddler as he seems very aggressive. He often wants me to build a tower of bricks so he can knock it down. Is this healthy or should I stop him?
Yours, Julia

Summary

- By playing, children learn how to be with others.
- Children can express feelings through play.
- Babies and toddlers do not share and cannot play cooperatively.
- Pre-school and school children have friendships and can play cooperatively.

Recognising children's different play needs

We have seen that play is very important to children's overall development. This means adults who work with children need to encourage all children to play. They also need to make sure that the play opportunities they are providing are the right ones for the children they are with.

Helping children with special needs

Some children may have special needs. They may need extra adult help or special equipment so they can play. There are many different reasons why children have special needs and it is important to find out what you need to do to help a child play.

Why might the children below lose out if adults do not look for ways of helping them?

> **Jo** finds it hard to walk and climb.
>
> **Michael** has only just joined the play group. He does not know any of the other children.
>
> **Kate** sometimes finds it hard to play with other children. She can be quite shy.
>
> **Gayetha's** skin is very sensitive and he cannot touch sand or dough.

Equal access

Equal access means all children getting the chance to do things. This may mean ensuring some children do not stop other children and ensuring that, if a child has a special need, they can still take part.

Look at some of the ways these children have been given equal access:

Gayetha has very sensitive skin	He wears gloves when he plays with dough and sand.
Jo finds it hard to walk and climb	An adult helps him and some activities are brought to him.
Kate is unsure of being with other children	An adult goes with her into the home corner.
Michael is new to the group	An adult stays near him until he has settled in.

Play and gender

Boys and girls have the same play needs. Some toys and activities may be seen as being for one gender rather than for both. For example, football is often seen as a boys' game, while playing house might be seen as a girls' game.

It is essential that adults encourage boys and girls to play with all the activities, as each play activity will encourage different skills. If children only play boys' or girls' games they will lose out (see also Stereotypes on page 151 – imaginative play).

- Encourage boys and girls to play with all the toys and equipment.
- Be careful not to say things that may make children feel things are only for one sex.
- Praise children for taking part and for playing.

Seeing children as individuals

It is important to realise that all children will have slightly different needs. This means they may need to play in different ways. Adults who work with children need to watch them and think about what they need. For example, a toddler who can push herself on a sit-and-ride toy might be ready for a tricycle. By looking at individual children, adults can help their development through play and find out what they enjoy playing with.

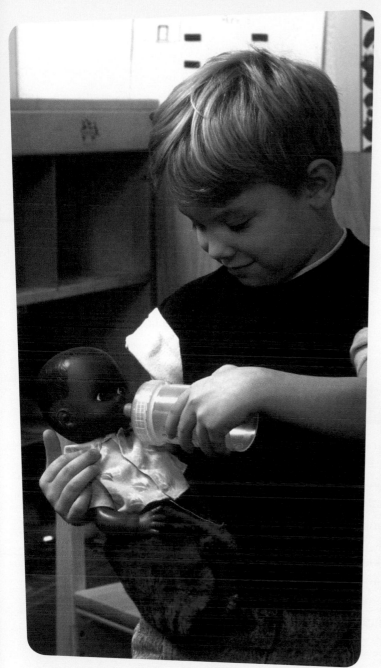

▲ Why is it important that boys also take on caring roles?

Case study

Tara likes dressing up. She is starting to put on hats and shoes. Mandy, the nursery assistant, has put out some capes and easy-to-pull-on skirts and trousers. Tara rushes over and tries to put them on.

What skill is Tara learning as she plays in the dressing-up area?

Activity

A mother tells the nursery manager that she does not want her daughter to be running around or kicking a ball 'like a boy'.

In pairs, decide why the nursery manager cannot agree to stop this from happening.

Summary

- All children have individual play needs.
- Some children may have special needs and adults must find ways of meeting these.
- It is important that all children in a setting have equal access to toys and equipment.
- Boys and girls have the same play needs and must have the same opportunities.

Indoor and outdoor physical play

When play will especially help children's physical development, it is sometimes called physical play. Physical play is very good for children's health and also gives them confidence. Look at some of the skills that children may develop during physical play:

- Jumping
- Balancing
- Cycling
- Walking
- Pedalling
- Dancing
- Throwing
- Catching
- Hopping
- Swinging
- Climbing
- Running.

Outdoor equipment and activities

Some equipment helps children's physical play because it provides them with challenges. Many children also make equipment part of their pretend play. For example, they might say that a climbing frame is a castle.

Indoor physical play

In some settings, physical play may be provided indoors. Some settings have halls or areas where large equipment can be used. In homes or smaller settings, adults have to find other ways.

Equipment	Age range	Benefits
Slides – small and large	Toddlers and older children	Children enjoy climbing and the feeling of sliding down. It helps their balance and their foot–eye coordination.
Trampolines	Toddlers and older children	Children enjoy bouncing. It strengthens their leg muscles and helps their balance.
Swings	Babies and all children	Children enjoy the movement. It helps their balance and, as they learn to swing themselves, builds up their coordination and leg muscles.
Play tunnels	Pre-school and older children	Children enjoy scrambling through. It helps their leg and arm movements.
Sit-and-ride toys, tricycles, bicycles, go-karts	Toddlers and all children	Many skills are developed – steering, pedalling, pushing and balance.
Climbing frames (small and large)	Toddlers and older children	Climbing makes children's legs strong. They also learn to balance and enjoy feeling 'on top'.
Seesaws and rockers	Toddlers and older children	Children enjoy rocking from side to side.
Balls, bean bags	Babies and all children	Babies enjoy seeing balls rolled to them and, at around nine months, being able to push balls themselves. Older children enjoy kicking, throwing and catching. These movements help children's hand–eye coordination and arm movements.
Hoops	Pre-school and older children	Hoops can be thrown, rolled and also climbed through. They help children's overall movements.

Action songs

Chasing bubbles

Throwing and catching – bean bags or foam balls

Prams and brick trolleys for children to push

Musical games such as 'Ring o' ring o' roses'

Ideas for physical play indoors

Music for all ages of children to move to (even babies who are mobile try to move)

Obstacle course

Treasure hunts

- Do not force children to try things they are unsure about.
- Encourage children by praising them and by offering them help.
- Make sure that children are safe.

Make sure equipment is safe and clean

Make sure equipment is right for the age/weight of children

Safety and physical play

Check outdoor play areas carefully (see pages 91 and 95)

Supervise children very carefully – look out for signs that children are overexcited or worried

Make sure equipment is being used correctly – e.g. children are sliding on the slide feet first

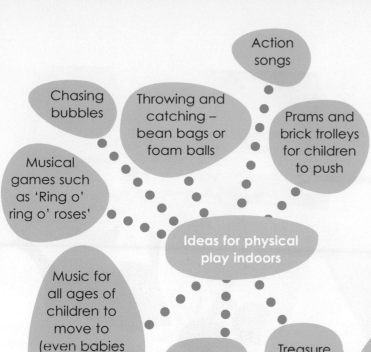

As well as gaining physical skills, children also gain confidence. What do you think this child is feeling?

The role of adults in providing physical play

Physical play needs to be carefully planned so that children can enjoy it in safety. It is also important to make sure activities are not too difficult so that children do not become bored or frustrated. Adults sometimes need to gently encourage children to try things. They may need to hold a child's hand or stay next to them when doing something new. Never force a child to do something they are afraid of, as they may lose their confidence.

- Find out what equipment and toys are available.
- Look carefully at children to see what they can already do.

Activity

A family wants to buy a piece of outdoor equipment for their children aged three and five years.

1 What would you suggest?

2 Give reasons for your choice.

Summary

- Physical play helps children's physical development.
- Physical play helps children's health and confidence.
- Physical play can be provided indoors and outdoors.
- It is essential to check that children are safe.

Creative play

Creative play is important because it helps children to express themselves. They may paint, draw or make things. All early years settings try to provide opportunities for creative play as there are many benefits for children.

Creative play must be creative!

For children to be creative, they need to have control and choice over what they are doing. Adults can help children, but it is important that they do not tell children what to do or what to use. The idea behind creative play is to allow children to express themselves as they want.

▲ What is this child learning by making this model?

Case study

Nadine is a nursery assistant. She wants all the children to make thank-you cards. She has chosen the paper, cut the shapes out and is telling the children how to stick the shapes on. She tells one boy off when he puts the shape in the 'wrong place'. Is this a good example of creative play?

Equipment for creative play

There are plenty of lovely materials available that will help children to draw, paint and make things. One starting point is to give children a choice of paper and card. There are many types of paper available, such as gummed paper, shiny paper, typing paper or coloured paper.

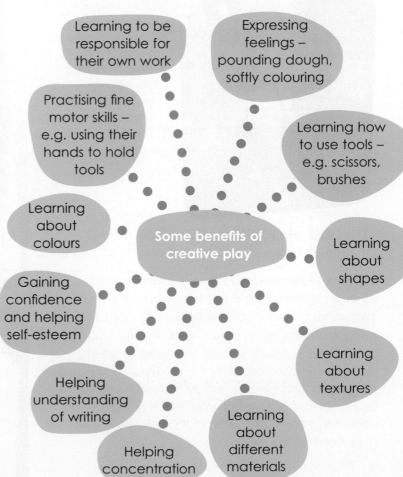

Some benefits of creative play

- Learning to be responsible for their own work
- Expressing feelings – pounding dough, softly colouring
- Practising fine motor skills – e.g. using their hands to hold tools
- Learning how to use tools – e.g. scissors, brushes
- Learning about colours
- Learning about shapes
- Gaining confidence and helping self-esteem
- Helping understanding of writing
- Learning about textures
- Helping concentration
- Learning about different materials

The role of the adult

Many settings put out several creative play activities – for example, a dough or clay table, a painting area and a drawing and collage table. Areas need to look inviting and interesting with enough items for children to feel they can play and make things. Equipment needs to be carefully chosen so children will be able to use it easily – for example, scissors that are easy to use or fabrics that are easy to cut.

- Ask children if they need any help.
- Make sure that left-handed children have left-handed scissors.
- Find out what they would like you to do.
- Do not take control over their work.
- Chat and listen to children as they work.
- Praise children for their ideas, rather than what they actually make.
- Praise children when they have difficulties and are able to continue concentrating.
- Name work and keep it safely.

Safety and hygiene – points to remember:

- Keep an eye on children when they use scissors.
- Do not use glitter with toddlers and supervise carefully as it can get in children's eyes.
- Supervise children if they are using staplers.
- Make sure dough has salt in it to prevent children from eating it.
- Check young children do not eat dough.
- Change dough regularly as it is handled.
- Make sure children wash their hands when they have finished.

Equipment for creative play

Painting

Different sizes of brush, choice of colours, sponges, things to print with

Drawing and mark making

Felt tip pens, rulers, chalks, markers, crayons, pencils, large and small wax crayons

Collage

Feathers (cleaned), ribbons, buttons, strips of lace, wood shavings, pipe cleaners, glitter (under supervision), magazines, photos, pasta and rice, strong glue

Junk modelling

Pipe cleaners, boxes of different shapes, strips of wood, staplers (under supervision), glue sticks, sticky tape

Sewing and weaving (pre-school and school children)

Choice of fabrics, scissors that cut, embroidery thread, wool, string, beads, ribbons

Clay and dough

Small tools, rolling pins, aprons

Activity

You have been asked to lay out a creative play table. The theme in the setting is black and white.

1 In pairs, think of as many things that you could put out on this table that would link to this theme.

2 What would you do if a child wanted to use a colour that was not white or black?

Summary

- Through creative play, children are able to express themselves.
- Creative play helps children gain confidence and develop fine motor skills.
- During creative play adults should help children rather than control what they do.

Imaginative play

Imaginative play is sometimes called role play or pretend play. During this type of play, children pretend to give toys characters or take on characters themselves.

Imaginative play is first seen in toddlers, with children of around 18 months often beginning to cuddle teddies or put dolls to bed. This type of play carries on sometimes until children are 12 or 13 years old, although these children might make it into proper plays with scenes and scripts.

This type of play helps children in many ways, including developing their language skills and social skills. It also helps them to express their feelings.

Toys and equipment for imaginative play

There are many different ways of providing imaginative play for children. Most settings have dressing-up clothes and home corners. Small toys such as farm animals and Play Mobil people are also used. These are sometimes called 'small world' toys.

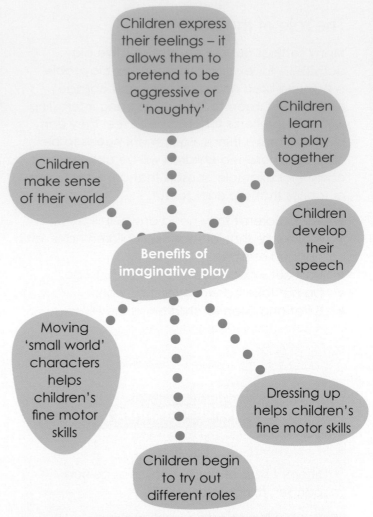

Children express their feelings – it allows them to pretend to be aggressive or 'naughty'

Children learn to play together

Children make sense of their world

Benefits of imaginative play

Children develop their speech

Moving 'small world' characters helps children's fine motor skills

Dressing up helps children's fine motor skills

Children begin to try out different roles

Equipment	Age range	Examples
Dressing-up clothes	Toddlers and all children	Everyday clothes that are easy to put on such as elasticated skirts, hats, shoes, including saris, tunics and scarves; outfits such as fire fighter, police officer, doctor
Small world play	Toddlers and all children	Farm animals; DUPLO® and LEGO®; Play Mobil people; Popoids
Cuddly toys	Toddlers and all children	Cuddly toys and dolls; covers and blankets; pram and brick trolley
Home corner	Pre-school and older children	Equipment found in most homes – e.g. cooker, sink, bed, table and chairs; cooking equipment
Puppets	Toddlers and all children	(Toddlers cannot use puppets but enjoy watching adults use them.) Finger and hand puppets; puppet theatre
Masks and face painting	Pre-school and older children	(Some children do not like wearing masks or having their face painted – always check beforehand.) Homemade masks; face paints (non-allergic)

The role of the adult

Toddlers and pre-school children often enjoy playing with adults. A toddler may give an empty cup and expect the adult to pretend to drink from it. Adults also need to make sure that a wide range of equipment is put out for children. This helps them to realise there is no single way of eating, cooking or dressing.

- Check that equipment is safe for children – e.g. some small world toys may not be suitable for toddlers.
- Make sure toys and equipment are clean.
- Check whether children are allowed face paints, in case of allergies.
- Play alongside toddlers and young children.
- Show children how equipment works – e.g. how to use a teapot or how you ask for a train ticket.
- Make sure dressing-up clothes are easy to put on and are clean.
- Listen out in case play becomes aggressive.
- Encourage children to try different roles and use a variety of equipment.

Stereotypes

A stereotype is a fixed idea of what groups of people are like – e.g. only women cook or only men can fix things. Stereotypes are not helpful, as they often stop children from trying out different activities. It is important to encourage children to take on a range of roles in their imaginative play – e.g. encourage girls to dress up as fire fighters and boys to mind the baby. It is also important to step in if children are saying things like, 'He can't do that because he's a boy.' Say things like, 'That's not actually true, of course he can do it, if he wants to.'

Learning through imaginative play

Many early years settings use imaginative play to help children learn about themes they are working on. They might create a shop or hospital. When this happens it is important that adults play alongside children so they can hear the language and know how to use the equipment.

Some ideas for themed imaginative play

- Train station
- Shoe shop
- Doctor's surgery
- Travel agent
- Petrol pump
- Takeaway
- Dental surgery
- Newspaper shop
- Restaurant
- Vet

Activity

1 In pairs, choose one of the ideas for themed imaginative play from above.

2 Make a list of equipment that could be used.

Summary

- Imaginative play can help children express their feelings.
- Many older children enjoy imaginative play.
- Some small world toys may not be suitable for very young children.
- It is important to step in if children are stopping others from joining in.

Knowing how to use equipment in real life helps children's imaginative play.

Sand and water play

Sand and water are traditional play materials and you will find them in many early years settings. Babies quickly learn to enjoy water and even adults enjoy showers and baths. There are many benefits from both of these materials.

Equipment

Most settings use specially designed sand and water trays. These are at the right height for children. Toys in the sand tray quickly become scratched and so many settings keep sand toys separate from other toys.

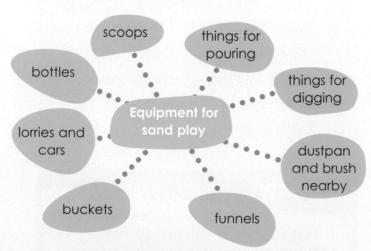

Equipment for sand play: scoops, things for pouring, bottles, things for digging, lorries and cars, dustpan and brush nearby, buckets, funnels

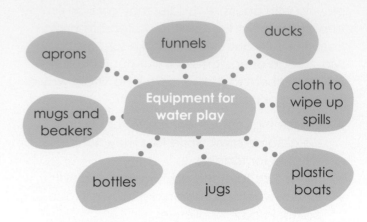

Equipment for water play: aprons, funnels, ducks, mugs and beakers, cloth to wipe up spills, bottles, jugs, plastic boats

The role of the adult

Children can learn a lot from sand and water. Many settings have sand and water out all the time. It is a good idea to change the equipment so children remain interested. Adults can help children learn if they talk to them about what they are doing. This will teach children new words like 'scoop' and 'dig'.

Benefits of sand and water play

Physical benefits
Develops fine motor skills through pouring, scooping, etc.

Cognitive benefits
Helps children to find out about volume and capacity.
Helps children's concentration.

Social benefits
Children often play next to each other or work with each other.

Language benefits
Many children will talk as they play.

Emotional benefits
Children enjoy playing with sand and water.
Children can release feelings by scooping, dropping and burying.
Water is known to relax children.

▲ Sand and water play needs to be supervised.

The role of the adult in sand and water play

Sand

- Hide shells and other 'treasure'.
- Make the sand wet or damp.
- Create an island from the sand.
- Put out dinosaurs and other animals.
- Damp sand down and encourage children to draw or print in it.
- Damp sand down and make sand castles complete with flags.

Water

- Help children to make boats.
- Colour the water.
- Put things out that will only float or only sink.
- Put out jugs of different sizes.
- Put ice cubes in the water to watch them float and melt.
- Put corks in the water tray to practise blowing them.

Safety and hygiene

Although sand and water are good fun, they can also be quite dangerous. Sand can get into children's eyes if it is thrown about. Children can drown in small amounts of water. This means that both areas should be very carefully supervised.

Case study

Jodie is flicking sand with a spade. She is three years old and is smiling. Harry watches her then starts to flick sand too. Mara, the supervisor, is watching. She tells them not to throw sand as it could get in their eyes and hurt them. She stays with them and shows them how to dig down. She praises them as they start to play carefully.

Making sand and water play safe

Sand

- Supervise the sand area very carefully.
- Do not allow children to throw sand around.
- Watch out for toddlers trying to eat sand.
- Only use proper 'silver' sand; not builders' sand.
- Clean sand after use with a sieve.
- Sweep up any sand straight away to stop children from falling.
- Throw away any sand that has got on the floor.
- Make sure children wash their hands after playing in the sand.

Water

- Never leave children alone near water.
- Change the water often so bacteria do not build up.
- Clean and rinse water toys so they stay clean.
- Wipe up any spills quickly so children do not fall over.
- Do not let children drink the water or put toys in their mouths.
- Dry the toys properly after use so they do not smell.
- Make sure children wash their hands after playing in the water.

Activity

A nursery assistant says that there is no point in putting out the sand as it makes too much mess and, in any case, the children don't really get much from it.

In pairs, work out what you could say to convince her otherwise.

Summary

- Sand and water play must be carefully supervised.
- Sand and water play are used in a lot of settings.
- Sand and water play provide many learning opportunities for children.

Construction play, block play and social play

These types of play are sometimes called manipulative play because children have to use their hands to manipulate the pieces. For example, they might put pieces of train track together or make a house out of bricks.

Toys and equipment

There are many types of toys and equipment for construction play. When choosing equipment, it is important to check the age range that it has been designed for. Toddlers can easily choke on small pieces.

The role of the adult

Many children enjoy playing with construction toys on the floor or on a table. It is important that there is enough space. If there are several children playing there need to be enough toys out. Sometimes children may need help to fix pieces together.

- Make sure that toys are stage/age appropriate.
- Be ready to help children if they are looking frustrated.
- Give suggestions to help children, but do not take control of their play.

▲ Construction play is sometimes called manipulative play.

Benefits of construction play

Physical benefits

Children use their fine motor skills to put pieces together.

Construction play helps strengthen the muscles in the hands.

Children's hand–eye coordination is developed as they put pieces together.

Language benefits

Children often talk as they are playing.

Children can learn new words – e.g. names of shapes, colours.

Emotional benefits

Children get a sense of achievement as they play.

Children learn to cope with a little failure – e.g. when a tower falls down.

Cognitive benefits

Children learn to concentrate and persevere.

Children learn about shape, size and colour.

Children learn to solve problems.

Children learn about structures – e.g. it is difficult to make a tall, thin tower out of bricks.

Construction play helps children's imagination.

Social benefits

Children often play side by side (parallel play).

Older children often cooperate on projects.

Equipment	Why?
Jigsaw puzzles	There are many different types of jigsaw puzzle. Toddlers enjoy ones where the pieces just lift out. As children get older they can do more complex puzzles.
DUPLO® and LEGO®	These popular toys combine construction play with imaginative play as many sets include people and characters. It is important not to leave LEGO® pieces near toddlers as the pieces are too small.
Interlocking train sets	Children enjoy train sets where the tracks fit together. They will need plenty of floor space.

Block play

Block play involves children using large or small wooden bricks and wooden shapes in order to make things such as houses, boats or whatever they are interested in. Block play helps children to think and problem-solve. It also helps children's physical skills as they have to balance blocks and move them around. As children become older, block play also provides opportunities to talk and play together. Many settings have block play outdoors as well as indoors.

Social play

Social play involves activities that encourage children to take turns, share and play together. Board games or cards and activities planned by adults can be used for this type of play.

What games did you enjoy playing when you were a child?

▼ Block play helps children to problem-solve and think.

Activity

1 In pairs, think of six objects that could be grouped together to help a three-year-old find out about the concept of hard and soft.

2 What were the reasons for your choices?

Summary

- Construction play encourages children to make things.
- Block play is important to help children think and build things.
- Social play encourages children to take turns, share and play together.

Stories and rhymes

It is never too early to read stories and sing rhymes to children. Babies love hearing rhymes and quickly learn to point out pictures in picture books. By nine months babies can enjoy rhymes such as pat-a-cake. Reading stories and joining in rhymes can help young children learn some of the skills they will need when they start to read. There are also other benefits.

Using rhymes with children

Babies and children will only learn rhymes if they hear them often enough. It is a good idea to use rhymes as part of a routine – for example, just before home time or during quiet times. Pre-school children also enjoy using 'props' during rhymes – for example, holding one of the five little ducks or a penny to buy a currant bun! Songs and rhymes can also help children if they are having to wait or are feeling unsettled.

Rhymes and action songs

Nursery rhymes and action songs help children to explore sounds and words. Research also shows that children who know their nursery rhymes get

off to a flying start with their reading! Counting rhymes can introduce children to numbers and counting. Most settings sing and teach children many different rhymes.

Babies and children enjoy sharing a book with an adult.

Popular nursery rhymes, counting rhymes and action songs

Counting rhymes
Five little ducks went swimming one day
Five fat sausages sizzling in the pan
Five currant buns in a baker's shop

Action rhymes
The wheels on the bus go round and round
Wind the bobbin up
I'm a little teapot
Pat-a-cake
Ring o' ring o' roses

Traditional nursery rhymes
Humpty Dumpty sat on a wall
Wee Willie Winkie
Sing a song of sixpence
Mary, Mary quite contrary

Benefits of stories and rhymes

Physical benefits
Action rhymes help physical development and coordination.
Turning over pages helps develop fine motor skills.

Cognitive benefits
Stories and rhymes help memory and concentration skills.
Older children gain knowledge from books.
Books and rhymes help children's imagination.

Emotional benefits
Babies and children enjoy sharing a book with an adult.
Stories that will help them to talk about their feelings can be read to them.

Language benefits
Picture books encourage babies to communicate.
Children become interested in learning to read.
Children learn about rhymes and rhythms.
Children learn how to handle books.

Social benefits
Pre-school and older children enjoy joining in with rhymes.

Choosing books for babies and children

There are many types of book for babies and children. It is important to choose the right type of book; otherwise children can become bored.

Books	Age range	Why
Simple picture books	Babies and toddlers	Simple pictures or photographs help babies learn words.
Picture books with a simple story	Toddlers and pre-school children	Short picture books are enjoyed by toddlers and pre-school children. It is important that the pictures are attractive and the text is easy to understand.
Pop-up books	Toddlers and older children	Pop-up books are very popular, but do not tend to last very long. Toddlers will need to be supervised when looking at them.
Big books	Pre-school and older children	These are used in settings so that all the children can see the text. They are also used in schools to teach children to read.
Fabric books	Babies and toddlers	These are used with babies and toddlers as they can be washed easily.

Sharing a story

Adults can share books with a single child or with groups of children. Sharing a book with a single child can be a special moment and can help children feel loved and cared for. Toddlers and pre-school children often bring a book they

want to read over to an adult. They often have favourite books they enjoy hearing over and over again. This can help them learn new words.

Telling a story to a group of children

- Read the book through by yourself first.
- Check the book is not too long or difficult.
- Ensure children are sitting comfortably.
- Ensure all children can see the book.
- Read the book with an interesting voice.
- Use props if possible.
- Show the pictures to the children.
- Check children are interested in the story.

Activity

In pairs, see if you can answer these questions about nursery rhymes.

1 What has sugar on the top?
2 What did the Knave of Hearts do?
3 What did the little boy who lived down the lane get?
4 What happened to Jack when he went to get water?
5 Whose garden had cockle shells in it?

Summary

- Children of all ages enjoy books and rhymes.
- Stories and rhymes help children's language development.
- Sharing stories can make children feel secure.
- Babies and children only learn rhymes if they are repeated frequently.

Music

Nearly everyone loves music and this begins very early on in life with babies enjoying lullabies and songs. Most early years settings have musical instruments and encourage children to dance and move to music.

Benefits of music and dance	
Physical benefits	Playing instruments helps develop fine and gross motor skills.
	Hand–eye coordination is needed to play some instruments – e.g. triangles.
	Moving to music helps develop gross motor skills.
Cognitive benefits	Making and moving to music can help children's imagination.
Emotional benefits	Children can express many emotions using music and dance.
	Children enjoy moving to music.
Social benefits	Children enjoy being with others when making or moving to music.
Language benefits	Music helps children listen.

▲ Young children benefit from music in many ways.

Types of musical instrument

There are many different types of musical instrument. Most young children enjoy shakers or instruments that they hit, such as tambourines and drums.

Making musical instruments

Although many settings may have 'proper' musical instruments, it is also possible to make simple instruments. Older children enjoy making and decorating their own instruments. Plastic screw-top bottles can be filled with rice, pasta or even coloured water to make simple shakers. Small shakers can be made using empty plastic containers and putting in a bell or some buttons.

Using musical instruments

Most toddlers love taking an instrument and exploring it. They may spend time banging it or shaking it. This is the first step towards enjoying music so, even if sometimes it sounds just like noise, it is important to let them play in this way. As children get older, they are able to shake or bang to a strong rhythm, so many settings start singing songs or putting on CDs and encouraging children to use their instruments in time.

- Check that instruments are safe for the age of children.
- Make sure there are enough instruments to avoid squabbles.
- Allow children to explore the instruments.
- Give children plenty of time.

Dance and moving to music

Most people, when they hear music with a rhythm, find they want to move to it. This even happens in babies, who often wriggle in time to music even though they cannot crawl. Moving to music helps children express their feelings as well as helping them to enjoy music.

Helping children to move to music: Young children find it easier to move to music when they can hear a strong beat or rhythm. Adults can give them ideas of how to move, but it is also good for children to move as they want. This helps them to express their feelings. Some settings have CDs that help children move to music, although very young children can find it hard to follow instructions.

- Make sure there is enough space for children to move safely.
- Look out for music that has a strong beat or tune.
- Join in so that children can gain ideas.

Follow my leader

This is a game for pre-school and older children. Ask the children to shake or bang their instruments whenever they see that your fingers are moving. They must stop when you put your hands together. This game can be varied by asking a child to be the leader.

Activity

Answer this email.

To:	marj@sunny-nursery.co.uk
From:	Jodie@hotmail.com
Date:	23 June 2001
Subject:	Three-year-old and tambourine

Hi Marjorie. You know about kids, don't you? I want to get my three-year-old a tambourine, but my partner says this will just be a waste of money. Is he right? Is there any other way I can help her enjoy music?
Jodie

Summary

- Babies and children enjoy music.
- Music can help children express their feelings.

Setting up for play and activities

An important part of working with children is setting up the activities, toys and equipment that they will need. In most settings this is done before children arrive, although during the session other equipment and toys may be put out to keep children playing happily.

Planning things to get out

Before setting up, it is a good idea to think about the points in the diagram below.

Preparing for play

There are many tasks that need doing before children can start playing. It is important to find out how your setting lays things out and the jobs that need doing (see the chart on page 161).

Making activities and toys look attractive

Children are likely to try out an activity or go to a play area if it looks interesting. This means that adults need to try to lay out equipment and toys attractively. It can be a good idea to start off some activities – e.g. put the first few pieces of a jigsaw puzzle together.

- **Dressing-up clothes**
  Hang clothes up; display some clothes.
- **Home corner**
  Lay out the table; put saucepans on the cooker.
  Dress dolls or teddies and make the bed.
- **Train set**
  Start off the track. Put trains on the track.

Does the setting already have some plans?	Many settings have plans which you may need to follow – check with your supervisor.
How many children are there in the setting?	Children need a choice of activities, but too many toys may overwhelm children – especially in a home setting.
What are children interested in doing?	Think about what you have seen children doing. How can you provide it again or help them to do similar things?
Are all areas of the curriculum covered?	Children need a variety of play as this is required by the Early Years Foundation Stage (England) and the Foundation Stage (Wales).
What do individual children need?	We always have to think about each child's interests and needs.

Area	Things to put out	Task
Paint	Fresh paints, clean brushes, pencil, paper, aprons.	• Make sure that painting areas look attractive. • Put out paper and aprons. • Make sure there are enough paints and brushes.
Writing area	Envelopes, paper, pencils, crayons, felt tips.	• Make sure there is enough paper. • Tidy away leftover paper. • Sharpen pencils.
Dough	Dough, cutters, rolling pins, aprons.	• Make up fresh dough if needed. • Wipe table and divide dough into pieces.
Sand and water	Sand and water trays, sand toys – e.g. scoops, buckets, spades, trucks – water toys – e.g. bottles, ducks, boats, cups – aprons, dustpan and brush, towels, clothes.	• Fill water tray with clean water. • Put out water toys. • Put out aprons. • Make sure there is a cloth and towel to hand. • Sieve sand to make sure it is clean. • Put out sand toys. • Make sure there is a dustpan and brush to hand. • Put out aprons.
Construction and small world toys	Duplo bricks, train sets, wooden bricks, farm animals.	• Put out groups of bricks, start off train set. • Create a scene.
Jigsaw puzzles	Jigsaw puzzles.	• Make sure puzzles are complete. • Place a few on a table. • Put one or two pieces in the jigsaw, put the others around it.
Creative area	Paper, glue, magazine cuttings, scissors, lace, feathers, glitter, small boxes.	• Put out equipment neatly. • Consider making something to show children.
Book corner	Books, cushions.	• Sort out books, put to one side books that need mending. • Make area attractive by standing some books up.
Home corner	Bedding, cups, plates, prams, dolls, cuddly toys.	• Set the table. • Make up the bed. • Dress dolls and toys. • Create a 'home' scene.
Outdoor play equipment	Slides, tricycles, hoops, benches, swings.	• Check for safety. • Dry the equipment, if wet. • Ensure there is enough equipment. • Arrange to look attractive.

Activity

Ann has joined an early years setting. On three mornings in a row, she has arrived just before the children. Other staff members are always there at least half an hour beforehand, to set up.

In pairs, work out how to explain to Ann the importance of arriving before the start of the session.

Summary

- Setting up is an important task in early years settings.
- It is important that children have everything they need to hand.
- Children will be interested in an activity if it is laid out attractively.

Selecting activities and resources

As well as encouraging children to learn by playing, most settings also organise some practical activities to help them gain some new skills. Activities that adults do with children are sometimes called **structured activities** or **adult-led activities**. This is because the adult has planned them.

Choosing activities

Children learn from playing because they are active in their learning and are doing things that interest them. This means the best activities are often those where children are busy doing things rather than listening or watching an adult.

Activities that link to particular needs of children

Looking at children's needs is a good starting point when planning activities. A child who finds it hard to throw and catch a ball may need an adult to do an activity with them such as throwing and catching bean bags.

Activities that link to the theme of a setting

In schools and early years settings, some activities may link to a theme. Interesting activities will help children learn more about a theme such as colours or homes.

Case study

Harry has been asked if he would like to make a clay pot. The theme is food in the nursery and one member of staff has shown the children how to make a simple thumb pot. Harry is making his pot and will be able to decorate it himself.

Activities that link to things that interest the child

Some activities might also be planned because they are of interest to the child. A child who spends a lot of time pretending to cook may enjoy doing some real cooking with an adult.

Case study

Mai is four years old and only speaks a little English. The play group leader has planned to help Mai learn the names of some of the toys in the setting. She has made a picture lotto game that has pictures of toys on it. By the end of the game, Mai knows the names of six toys.

Case study

Barney is fascinated by minibeasts. His nanny has found him a magnifying sheet and he loves looking at bugs through it.

Matching activities to children's development

In Unit 2 we looked at children's development. Adults who work with children have to match children's development to the practical activities they plan for them. This is important so that children do not find it hard to concentrate and to ensure they enjoy an activity. Most settings ask children if they are interested in doing an activity, as a child who is keen will learn and concentrate.

Putting out toys, equipment and resources

In this unit we have seen that different types of play promote different skills in children. This means that, as well as some practical activities, children in early years settings will also need a range of different things to play with.

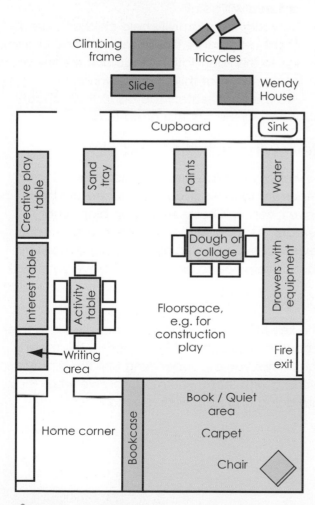

How many different types of play are there in this setting?

Common activities

Babies 0–6 months: Discovery play, contact directly with the baby – e.g. cuddling and talking to the baby.

Babies 6–12 months: Discovery play, sensory activities – e.g. play with cold cooked spaghetti or jelly; opportunities to play games with adults – e.g. pat-a-cake.

Toddlers: Discovery play, sensory activities – e.g. corn flour and water, cooked spaghetti, sponge printing.

Pre-school children: Games like picture lotto, cooking, feely bags, throwing and catching.

School children: Games like snakes and ladders, cooking, nature trails, treasure hunts, obstacle courses, team games like simple rounders.

Activity

In pairs, think about activities that these children might enjoy doing.

1 Tara is three years old. Next week she is going into hospital to have an operation.
2 Curran is four years old and, while painting, has noticed that the yellow paint has run into the blue and made a green colour.
3 Rahima is two years old and loves listening and dancing to music.

Summary

- Practical activities can help children learn new skills.
- Activities must be right for the children's stage of development.
- Children prefer activities that are fun and where they can be active.
- It is a good idea to change toys and equipment so children do not get bored.

Planning and reviewing play and activities

Most early years settings plan the play session carefully. This means children's needs can be met and staff will know what they should be doing.

Planning play and activities

Before planning play and activities, think through these questions:

How many children will there be?	It is important to make sure there is enough equipment and resources for the number of children.
What are the ages of the children?	You need to make sure equipment and resources are safe for the age of children and right for their stage of development.
What are the needs of the children?	It is important to think about individual children as well as how to promote the development of all the children.
How long is the session or how long will the activity take?	The amount of time children are in the session will make a difference to how much they can do.
What equipment, toys and resources are available?	There is no point in planning play or activities if the equipment needed is not available!

Planning is important to:

- meet individual children's needs
- promote children's development
- help adults in the setting feel organised
- make sure resources are available
- help the smooth running of the setting
- make sure children will enjoy the session
- make sure everyone knows what equipment should be put out.

Activity plans

Most students find it helpful to draw up an activity plan to use as a guide. There are different ways of laying them out, but all activity plans should show that you can plan to meet the needs of the children you are working with. You should include the following in your activity plan:

- What will you be doing?
- Why have you chosen to do this activity?
- How many children can do this at once?
- How old are the children?
- Where will this be happening?
- How long will the activity take?
- What equipment will need to be put out or prepared?
- What skills or knowledge are you hoping children will gain?
- How might this activity help children's areas of development? (Some settings may also link this to the Foundation Stage or the early years curriculum that they are following.)
- Are there any safety factors to think about?
- What will the adult(s) need to do?

Reviewing activities and play

As well as planning play and activities, it is also important to think about how successful they have been. This helps settings to plan other sessions. As a student, you will find you need to review activities and play that you have set up. This will help you to learn and improve your work.

Observing children

The key to reviewing play and activities is to think about the reactions of the children. This means that, while you are supervising children's play or working with them, you must observe what they are doing and note their reactions.

Were the children interested in the play or the activity? How long did they concentrate for?

If the children are interested and stay for some time, this usually means the activity was right for their stage of development and met their needs.

What was the behaviour of the children?

Unwanted behaviour, such as throwing toys around, can be caused by play and activities not being right for the needs of the children. They might be bored or frustrated or there might not be enough equipment out.

Did the children play in the way you expected?

Sometimes children find their own way of playing or carrying out activities. For example, a child might make a card out of their collage rather than a flat picture. This helps us to learn about what they enjoy doing and can help us plan for the next time.

As well as thinking about the children's reactions to an activity or play, we also need to think about how easy we found it.

Did the activity or play take longer to prepare than you thought?

Remember this for next time and make sure that you allow enough preparation time.

What parts of the activity did you think went well?

Try to work out why things seemed to work – was it because you had thought about the needs of the children?

What would you improve if you were planning this again?

Think about how to improve your planning or the way you work with children. Ask your supervisor or tutor for advice.

Using reviews

Some settings review what has happened after each session, while others may do so in staff meetings. It is important to plan using information from the reviews so that children's needs can be met. As a student, you may need to write down your review so your supervisor and/or tutor can see what you have learned.

Activity

Look back at the activity on page 163. Write an activity plan for one of the activities you suggested.

Summary

- Planning helps settings meet children's needs.
- Planning helps staff to be organised.
- Reviewing sessions can help future planning.
- It is important to look at children's reactions during play and activities.

The role of the adult in supporting play and learning

Children need adults to help them play and also to help them learn. Being a good early years worker is more than just supervising children and letting them play.

The role of the adult involves:

- checking play is safe
- seeing if children need help
- looking for ways to encourage children
- talking and asking children questions so they learn from what they are doing

- showing children skills
- helping children play with each other
- getting out extra equipment and resources if children need it
- playing alongside children.

Watching and listening to children

There are many ways adults can help children while they are playing or doing activities. Watching and listening to children helps us decide what we need to do. Look at the chart below.

Watch and listen	Why
Look at children's faces • Do children look interested? • Are children concentrating?	Children who look bored or unhappy will need an adult to support them.
Look at children's body language • Are there any signs of boredom? • Do children seem tired – e.g. sucking thumb?	Children who seem bored or tired may need an adult to work with them.
See how children are playing • Are children playing with each other? • Are there any children who are looking left out or unsure? • Is the play challenging and interesting? • Are they playing safely? • Is there enough equipment?	Decide whether children need to be helped in their play.
Listen to children as they are playing • Do they seem happy and content? • Are the children squabbling? • Are there loud angry voices?	Sometimes children's voices might tell us that there is a problem.

Playing alongside children

One of the ways we might help children is by playing alongside them. For example, you might be a player in a game, such as picture lotto, to help children take turns with each other or you might join in a toddler's imaginative play by pretending to be poorly.

By playing alongside children, you can help them learn new words and how to use equipment.

Case study

A group of children are throwing bean bags in the air. Androv goes over and shows the children how to aim at an object. He joins in and stays with them until they seem to be able to manage themselves.

Putting out more resources

Sometimes children need extra toys or equipment in order to play, as they might be running out of ideas. This will help them to enjoy the activity or play more. It might also help if children are squabbling because they all want to play with the same toys or equipment.

Helping children

Quite often children need a little bit of adult help. It is important to offer help rather than jump in and take control. Offering to help means that children can still feel they are doing things for themselves, which gives them confidence.

Case study

Frank is trying to make a model, but the pieces keep falling off. Yasmin asks him if he would like to use some sticky tape instead of the glue.

▲ Why is it important to offer help to children?

Intervening in children's play

There are times, when children are playing, when adults must intervene:

- when they might hurt themselves
- when they might hurt others
- if equipment or toys might get broken
- if children are being unkind to other children
- when children are showing signs of frustration
- when children are running out of ideas about what to do.

Case study

Chris notices that Alicia is struggling to put on some dressing-up clothes. He asks her if she wants a hand. She lets him help and then runs off to carry on playing in the home corner.

Activity

Simon and Rufus have been playing well together at the water tray. They have just started to pour water onto each other's sleeves.

1 Why do you think this is happening?

2 How might the adult be able to help them carry on playing?

Summary

- It is important for adults to watch and listen to children's play.
- Adults must always intervene if children are likely to hurt themselves or others.
- It is better if adults offer children help rather than take control of activities.
- Sometimes adults need to put out new toys and equipment so children do not get bored.

Choosing equipment

We have seen that toys and equipment can help children to learn. Choosing what to put out is a skill. The Early Years Foundation Stage (England) and Foundation Stage (Wales) require settings to make sure that a wide range of play opportunities are available and that they link to the curriculum.

Looking at the play value of toys and equipment

Some of the best toys and equipment can be used in more than one way – for example,

construction bricks such as DUPLO® can be used to make houses, buildings, cars and trains. This means children can pick them up and use them in different ways and will not get tired of them. Toys and equipment that have good play value might also appeal to children of slightly different ages. Balls and hoops, for example, can be used in several ways and appeal to children of different ages.

The following chart shows some equipment that is often used with children. Notice how some toys and equipment can be used by more than one age group.

Age (years)	Indoor equipment	Outdoor equipment
1–2	• Push-and-pull toys • Toys that make music • Dolls and cuddly toys • Trolleys and prams • Building bricks • Posting and stacking toys	• Paddling pool • Baby swing • Small slide
2–3	• Dressing-up clothes • Home corner equipment • DUPLO® or other building bricks • Toy cars and garages • Small world toys • Jigsaw puzzles • Musical instruments • Sand and water trays	• Paddling pool • See-saws • Slide • Climbing frame • Swings • Sit-and-ride toys • Tricycles • Balls
3–4	• Small world toys • Dressing-up clothes • Home corner equipment • Water, sand and dough • Prams • Construction toys – e.g. train sets, DUPLO® • Jigsaw puzzles	• Paddling pool • Slide • Climbing frame • Swings • Tricycles • Balls, bean bags, footballs • See-saws

Age (years)	Indoor equipment	Outdoor equipment
4–6	<ul><li>Small world toys</li><li>Dressing-up clothes</li><li>Home corner equipment</li><li>Water, sand and dough</li><li>Construction toys – e.g. train sets, DUPLO® and LEGO®</li><li>Prams</li><li>Jigsaw puzzles</li><li>Simple board games</li><li>Card</li></ul>	<ul><li>Paddling pool</li><li>Slide</li><li>Climbing frame</li><li>Swings</li><li>Bicycles (with stabilisers)</li><li>Balls, bean bags, footballs</li><li>Hoops, benches</li><li>Gardening tools</li></ul>

Increasing the play value of toys

Sometimes we can increase the play value of toys and equipment by putting them with other equipment. Tricycles that are next to dressing-up clothes can help children enjoy using the tricycle while taking part in imaginative play.

Ensuring safety

It is always important to check that toys and equipment are suitable for the age of the children. Toys and equipment can also become broken and parts can become loose and dangerous. This means that toys and equipment must always be checked for safety.

Ensuring children's safety – The role of the adult

Do	Don't
Supervise at all times	Leave children playing alone
Check that toys are suitable for the age of the children	Put out toys that babies might swallow
Follow the manufacturer's instructions	Put out toys that are designed for older children
Put the lid on sand and water when not in use	Leave children playing near water

Safety marks

Toys and equipment should have safety marks on them. This means they meet with regulations and should be safe.

Second-hand equipment

Some settings and families cannot afford new things so they buy second-hand. These toys and equipment need to be cleaned and checked very carefully before being used.

Activity

A family has two children aged three and five years. In pairs, choose five toys or pieces of equipment that would be suitable for both children to play with at home.

Summary

- There are many factors to think about when buying or choosing equipment.
- Toys and equipment should have safety marks on them.
- Toys and equipment that allow children to play in different ways are often good value.
- Second-hand equipment must be checked very carefully.

End of unit summary

End of unit task: Children's play poster

Copy out and complete the charts below.

Use the information from your charts to make a poster about play that shows how different types of activities can help children's development and how adults can help support play. You can use pictures of children and equipment to decorate your poster.

Equipment/ activity	Type of play	Suitable for children aged	Benefits of this activity
Playing on the swings	Physical – outdoor	6 months– 12 years	Helps children to balance
DUPLO® bricks	Construction		
Sand			
Water			
Dressing-up corner			
Farm set			
Picture lotto			
Dancing to music			
Treasure basket play			

Supporting children's play – the role of the adult	
DO	DON'T
Supervise at all times	Leave children playing alone
Check that toys are suitable for the age of the children	Put out toys that babies might swallow

Back to the real world

You should now understand how play is used to promote children's development. You have learned about different types of play; both indoors and outdoors. You should also be able to choose appropriate resources and equipment.

1 Can you list three pieces of equipment or toys that would support a four-year-old's fine motor skills?

2 Can you explain how play supports children's social and emotional development?

3 Can you list three pieces of equipment that might be used for sand and water play?

Glossary

adult-led activities Play or activities where the adult tells or shows children what to do

cooperative play Children are playing together

mastery play Play where young children repeat their actions

parallel play Two or more children are playing near each other, but not with each other

spectator play A child watches other children playing

structured activities Activities that have been set out for children to learn certain things

symbolic play Play where children pretend that objects stand for other things

My story

Melanie, Teaching assistant

I have been working alongside the reception teacher for nearly a year now. I love the job because a lot of my time is involved in setting up play opportunities and also observing children. I had thought that I would be doing more 'teaching', but the Early Years Foundation Stage means that children are mostly learning through play. I often play board games or read stories to small groups of children. One of my jobs in the morning is to set up the outdoor play area. We have free flow play and the outdoor area is shared with the nursery. We go out in all weather and so I have had to buy a really warm coat!

Unit 7 Orientation to work programme

The aim of this unit is to help you think about your future. It looks at the skills that you will need in order to start work under supervision. You will learn about child protection and how to manage children's behaviour.

The unit will also help you to understand the main laws that settings must stick to. At the end of the unit, you will need to consider what type of childcare settings you would like to work in. You will also learn about the type of further training that you might need. This unit covers the following:

- basic principles of effective work with children
- how to work in a childcare setting
- how to plan the next step of your career and/or education and training.

The topics you will find in this unit are:

- Understanding children's behaviour
- Promoting positive behaviour
- Safeguarding children
- Working in a childcare setting
- The main laws relating to working with children
- Planning your next step

In the real world

You are not sure whether you want to take a further course or look for a job in childcare with training. Your placement supervisors says that if you are going to start in a nursery, you must have some knowledge of child protection and managing children's behaviour.

By the end of this unit, you will have a clearer idea of your next step and a basic knowledge of child protection and managing children's behaviour.

Understanding children's behaviour

Adults who work with children need to understand and manage their behaviour. To do this effectively, we have to meet the needs of children and understand them.

Respecting and valuing children

Children's behaviour can sometimes be like a mirror. Children who feel good about themselves often show wanted behaviour, while children who do not feel valued may show **unwanted behaviour**. This means that adults have to make every child feel valued and respected. The best way to do this is by really getting to know children so we understand them.

- Never have favourite children.
- Get to know children and be interested in what they are doing.

Having realistic expectations

It is important to understand what children can and cannot do at different ages. This stops us expecting too much (or too little) of children. Expectations must be fair, otherwise children will feel they are failing. A two-year-old may snatch a toy, but this is to be expected as this age group cannot share. This means the adult needs to handle the situation differently from if a six-year-old snatches. (See also Unit 2 for more information on children's development.) The chart on page 175 shows some of the stages of development for children at different ages and the types of behaviour to encourage. These are **goals for behaviour**, and adults should praise children when they meet the goals.

Making sure that children's needs are met

Before managing children's behaviour, it is important to recognise the reasons behind it. On pages 110–11 we looked at the needs of children. If any of these needs are not being met, children may show unwanted behaviour. It is important to try to meet these needs as this will change the behaviour.

Hunger, tiredness and temperature

Children who are hot, hungry and tired will often show unwanted behaviour. They may become aggressive, irritable or clingy. Children aged two to three years may have tantrums!

Feeling insecure

Insecurity may make some children clingy, tearful or withdrawn. Other children become aggressive and challenging. There are many reasons why children feel insecure – for example, they might be new in a setting or something might have changed at home, such as a new baby, family death, separation or divorce of parents.

Lack of stimulation

Children may show unwanted behaviour if they are bored or want some adult attention. This means we must make sure children are able to play and have some attention from us.

Age	Stage of development	Goals for behaviour
1–2 years	• May not stay with one toy or activity. • Explores actively. • Repeats actions that gain attention. • Has no understanding that toys or other objects may belong to others. • Is not aware of others' needs or feelings.	• To carry out very simple instructions – e.g. wave bye bye. • To play alongside, but not with, other children.
2–3 years	• Is easily frustrated and may have tantrums. • Has no understanding of the need to wait. • Finds sharing very difficult. • Want to do things for themselves, but may get frustrated. • May show aggressive behaviour. • May stay at one type of play or activity when interested.	• To wait for a few minutes before needs are met. • To share toys or food with one other child with adult help (not favourite things). • To play alongside other children with adult help. • To say please and thank you when reminded.
3–4 years	• Is beginning to use language to explain what they want. • Can play cooperatively most of the time – may need help from adults. • Can share and take turns most of the time, although there may be some squabbles. • Occasional tantrums; especially if overtired or hungry.	• To share and take turns. • To follow instructions most of the time. • To tidy away with adult's help.
4–5 years	• Plays with other children without help from adults. • Is able to say what they are feeling and explain their wishes. • Is beginning to understand the need for rules.	• To ask permission before taking other children's toys. • To comfort playmates in distress. • To tidy up after activities.
5–8 years	• Has strong friendships – may get upset if they fall out. • Can argue back or put forward own point of view. • Has many self-help skills – can get dressed, wipe up spills, collect things they need. • Will concentrate for long periods on play or activities that interest them.	• To apologise to others. • To listen to others. • To sit quietly when needed. • To be helpful and thoughtful.

Activity

In pairs decide whether these are fair expectations. Use the chart on this page and information from Unit 2 to help you decide.

1 Most two-year-olds should be able to dress themselves.
2 Most four-year-olds can wait their turn before going down the slide.
3 Most three-and-a-half-year-olds can play with other children.
4 Most five-year-olds should be able to help tidy up.

Summary

• Children are more likely to show wanted behaviour if they feel valued and respected.
• Adults need to have realistic expectations of children.
• Children may show unwanted behaviour if their needs are not being met.

Promoting positive behaviour

Children need adults to meet their needs and guide their behaviour. What is considered **positive behaviour** can vary from person to person, but most people agree that children need to learn to treat other people with respect. To do this, children need to learn some self-control as well as some skills such as sharing, taking turns and listening to others.

How children learn positive behaviour

There are two main ways children learn behaviour:

- by copying others
- by positive reinforcement.

Copying others

Children can learn how to share, say thank you and take turns by watching others and copying them. This means adults who work with children need to set a good example by showing them how to behave. This is sometimes called being a good role model.

▲ What are these children learning from watching the adult help them?

Case study

Three-year-old Rajeet sees that a nursery assistant holds the door open for some children to go through. He goes up to the nursery assistant and tries to help her hold open the door.

Case study

Mandy pulls off a piece of dough and gives it to the girl next to her. An adult smiles at her and says 'Well done, Mandy, that was kind to give it to Samantha.' Mandy is more likely to share again in the future.

Positive reinforcement:

Children enjoy attention, praise and treats. These are **positive reinforcements**, or rewards. If children get rewards for wanted behaviour, they are likely to repeat the action.

It is important not to give any positive reinforcements for behaviour that we do not want children to repeat; otherwise the child will repeat it again. This sometimes means ignoring a child rather than giving any attention.

Ways we can help children

As well as praising children when they show wanted behaviour and being good role models, we can also help by letting them know what we are expecting of them. This is sometimes called **boundary setting**. It is always a good idea to set the boundaries before children need them – a little like knowing the rules of the game before it starts.

- Make sure your expectations are fair for the age of the child.
- Be clear so that the child knows what you are expecting.
- With pre-school and older children explain the reason for the boundary.

Case study

Clare is making a scraping sound with her chair. She looks over to the nursery assistant as she does this. The nursery assistant tells her not to do it. Clare smiles and does it again.

1 Why does Clare smile?

2 Why might it have been better to have ignored the behaviour?

'After this we'll need to tidy up.'	This lets the child know what is expected of them.
'We'll need to be very quiet for a moment because everyone else is listening to the music.'	The reason for the boundary has been explained.
'I think that you'll enjoy playing in the sand, but remember: we don't throw sand, do we?'	This reminds the children about safety

Learning acceptable behaviour is a gradual process

Children are not born with self-control and the ability to share and take turns. It is important to remember this and look at children's stages of development. We may need to change our approach with different ages of children, but good supervision and praise are needed with all children.

Age	Behaviour	Adult role
1–2 years	Have no sense of danger	<ul><li>Distract children</li><li>Praise wanted behaviour</li><li>Ignore unwanted behaviour</li></ul>
2–3 years	Are easily frustrated Need adult attention	<ul><li>Praise wanted behaviour</li><li>Be consistent</li><li>Ignore unwanted behaviour</li></ul>
3–4 years	Need adult attention and praise	<ul><li>Set boundaries</li><li>Praise wanted behaviour</li><li>Be a good role model</li></ul>
4–5 years	Can get overexcited during play	<ul><li>Explain the need for boundaries</li><li>Praise wanted behaviour</li><li>Provide interesting activities</li></ul>

Activity

Angie has just started work at a play group. She sees a two-year-old child snatch a piece of dough from another child. Angie goes and snatches the piece back. The child begins to cry, but Angie says, 'Now you know what it feels like.'

1 In pairs, think about whether this was the best way of handling the child's behaviour.

2 Decide how you might have handled the behaviour.

Summary

- Sharing, taking turns and thinking of others are all types of behaviour that we want to encourage.
- Adults need to think about the ages of the children.
- Praise and attention will help children repeat wanted behaviour.
- Adults need to be good role models.

Safeguarding children

As well as keeping children safe from hazards, adults must also keep children safe from **abuse**. Some settings use the term 'child protection' while others talk about 'safeguarding children'. Every setting will have a policy. You will need to read the policy in your setting as well as these pages.

What is abuse?

There are four main types of abuse but, in general, it means that children are being badly treated in some way. Abuse can happen in a child's home and be carried out by a family member or friend, as well as by strangers outside the home. There have also been cases where adults working with children have abused them.

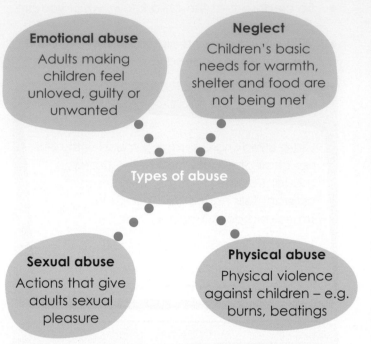

Emotional abuse
Adults making children feel unloved, guilty or unwanted

Neglect
Children's basic needs for warmth, shelter and food are not being met

Types of abuse

Sexual abuse
Actions that give adults sexual pleasure

Physical abuse
Physical violence against children – e.g. burns, beatings

Type of abuse	Physical signs	Behaviour
Physical abuse	<ul><li>Bite marks.</li><li>Bruising on areas of non-accidental injury.</li><li>Burns and scalds.</li></ul>	<ul><li>Aggressiveness towards other children.</li><li>Seems unsure of how they gained the injury.</li><li>Unwilling to change – e.g. take off jumper or cardigan.</li></ul>
Emotional abuse	<ul><li>Failure to thrive.</li></ul>	<ul><li>Extreme attention seeking and clinginess.</li><li>Telling lies.</li><li>Stammering or stuttering.</li><li>Tantrums in older children.</li></ul>
Sexual abuse	<ul><li>Wetting or soiling in older children.</li><li>Pain when going to the toilet.</li><li>Bruises, unexplained scratch marks.</li><li>Itchiness or soreness in genital areas.</li></ul>	<ul><li>Sexual knowledge in play.</li><li>Sexual knowledge in drawings.</li><li>Withdrawn behaviour.</li><li>Regression – i.e. wanting to be treated like a baby or younger child.</li></ul>
Neglect	<ul><li>Dirty skin and hair.</li><li>Underweight.</li><li>Constant colds and infections.</li><li>Many bumps and bruises from accidents.</li></ul>	<ul><li>Often hungry.</li><li>Poor concentration.</li><li>Tired and may fall asleep.</li></ul>

Identifying when a child is being abused

Adults working with children must keep an eye out for possible signs of abuse, as children will often not tell adults there is a problem. The chart on page 178 shows some of the signs of abuse that children under eight years may show.

What to do if you suspect a child has been abused

Many children are afraid of telling an adult they are unhappy. This means we must be aware of any injuries or other signs of abuse. If you see a child with a bruise or bump, ask them how it happened and if they are all right. Most children enjoy telling adults about injuries! Always tell your supervisor if you have any worries about a child in your setting.

What to do if a child tells you he or she has been abused

It can be very hard for children to tell someone they have been abused so you must always take them seriously.

- Tell them you will help them but that, to do this, you must tell someone else.
- Tell them they were right to tell an adult.
- Do not ask the child any questions as the case could be referred to the police.
- Find your supervisor and tell them what has happened. They will then contact the local child protection team. You may be asked to write down what the child said to you.

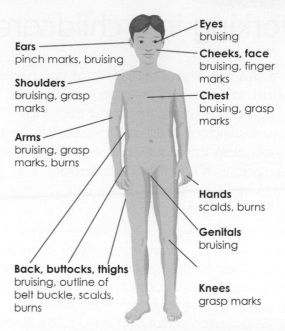

Eyes
bruising

Ears
pinch marks, bruising

Cheeks, face
bruising, finger marks

Shoulders
bruising, grasp marks

Chest
bruising, grasp marks

Arms
bruising, grasp marks, burns

Hands
scalds, burns

Genitals
bruising

Back, buttocks, thighs
bruising, outline of belt buckle, scalds, burns

Knees
grasp marks

▲ Areas of the body where bruises and bumps may be the result of abuse rather than accidents.

Activity

It is a very hot day and you notice that Robin still has his jumper on. You suggest he takes it off, but he looks quite upset and clings to it. Later on you notice he screams with pain when another child bumps into his back. When you ask him if he is all right, he just nods his head.

How would you handle this situation?

Case study

Ashrak has a black eye. His mother said he had fallen down the stairs. At playtime he holds the nursery assistant's hand. She asks him how he got his bump. He looks at the ground and says he had been naughty and his mum hit him. The nursery assistant waits until Ashrak has gone off with his friend and then finds the class teachers.

Summary

- Adults working in settings must read the child protection or safeguarding children policies.
- Adults must look out for signs of child abuse.
- Abuse can be carried out by family members, friends or adults working with children, as well as strangers.
- If you have any worries about children you must talk to your supervisor.

Working in a childcare setting

There are a number of skills that you need to show to work in a childcare setting. As well as health and safety and thinking about individual children's needs, you must also be able to work with both parents and other adults. It is quite a package!

Working with parents

Parents are very important in children's lives. They know their children, take care of them and want the best for them. By working with parents, settings can find out about children's needs and help children to settle in. Parents also like to be given information about how their child is doing, so many settings spend time talking to parents at the start and end of sessions.

Passing on information

As a student or junior member of staff, you must not tell parents what you think about their child's progress or answer any queries. This information should be passed on to your supervisor or team leader. You must also be careful not to breach confidentiality by talking about other people's children.

Working with other adults

As well as being able to work with parents, practitioners also have to work with other adults. Most settings work with other people who support either the setting or children – for example, a speech therapist might come in to help staff work with a child whose language is developing very slowly.

- Respect and be courteous to all adults in settings.
- Remember that children or issues being discussed may be confidential.
- Do not pass on information unless you have checked first with your supervisor.

Talking to parents

- Find out how parents like to be addressed – e.g. Mrs Peters or Jo.
- Greet parents with a smile – do not ignore them.
- Listen carefully to parents.
- Show parents that you have noticed and enjoy working with their child.
- Be polite at all times.

Can work with parents

Understands confidentiality

Calm

Enthusiastic

Reliable

Aware of safety

Meets children's needs

Knowledge of children's development

Can work in a team

Takes the initiative

Follows policies and procedures

Plans appropriate learning activities

▲ Look at the knowledge and skills needed in a good childcare practitioner. What knowledge and skills have you already gained? Can you link these skills to the units covered?

Working as part of a team

Teamwork is very important in childcare settings as they are busy places. In the first unit, we looked at the skills of teamwork (pages 20–21). Most teams have staff meetings to help them plan and talk about their work.

Advisers give advice to settings about their practice.

Support teachers help children with learning difficulties.

Physiotherapists help children with their physical development.

Adults who may visit or be in settings

Health visitors advise parents on the health and development of their children.

Speech therapists help children with their language development.

Helpers are unpaid volunteers.

Inspectors check the quality of settings.

Activity

1 In pairs look at the following statements and give yourself a mark out of 10.

- I know about safety and hygiene.
- I treat each child as an individual
- I am never late for work.
- If I am unsure, I always ask for help.
- I always look for ways of helping other team members.
- I am cheerful when I am working.
- I never gossip.

2 Practitioners need many skills to work with children.

In pairs, think of three ways you could become a better practitioner.

Summary

- Practitioners must have a range of skills.
- Practitioners must be able to work with parents and other adults.
- Teamwork is important in childcare settings.

The main laws relating to working with children

All childcare settings have policies and procedures that must be followed. These are very important as they are often based on legal requirements – for example, a setting must store cleaning fluids properly; otherwise they would be breaking the Health and Safety at Work Act.

Did you know?

- The UK is split into four countries – Scotland, Northern Ireland, England and Wales.
- Each country has its own system of education and inspection.
- Some of the laws vary.

Childcare Act 2006 (England only)

This is an important law. It means that all early years settings, including childminders, have to follow the Early Years Foundation Stage (EYFS) framework. It also means that settings are inspected by Ofsted.

▲ Why is it important that settings keep to the staff to child ratio?

Settings must follow the education programme of the EYFS

Settings must be inspected by Ofsted

Settings must provide a balance of child-initiated play and adult-led activities

Key points of the Childcare Act

Staff to children ratios must be followed

Settings must carry out observations on children

Children must have time in and out of doors

Settings must have a safeguarding children policy

All children must have a key person

Health and Safety at Work Act 1974

The Health and Safety at Work Act was written to make sure that employees are kept safe.

Settings must follow fire regulations

Settings must risk assess how they store chemicals

Settings must have a first aider and a first aid box

Key points of the Health and Safety at Work Act

Employees must use the safety equipment provided by their employers

Employees must report anything that might be a danger

Special Education Needs and Disability Act 2001

The Special Education Needs and Disability Act placed requirements on education providers not to discriminate against disabled people.

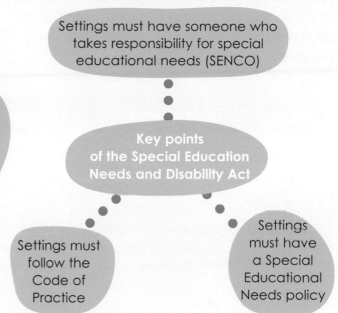

Settings must have someone who takes responsibility for special educational needs (SENCO)

Key points of the Special Education Needs and Disability Act

Settings must follow the Code of Practice

Settings must have a Special Educational Needs policy

Safeguarding Vulnerable Groups Act 2006

Anyone who wants to work with children or adults who may need extra help must be checked out before they are allowed to work with them.

Activity

Find out what policies your placement has to have.

Summary

- Settings have a range of policies and procedures. These are based on legal requirements.
- Practitioners must read the policies in their setting.
- Settings are inspected to check that children are being cared for properly.

Planning your next step

There are many opportunities to work with children and it is important to decide what your next steps will be. To do this you will need to find out about job opportunities in your area and the qualifications that you will need.

Work opportunities

Look at this table and think about the type of work you might like to do. Your tutor or career adviser should also be able to tell you more about other work and qualifications.

Job	Type of work	Skills needed	Qualifications
Play worker	Works with children usually aged 4–15 years during holidays or after school	• Ability to work with several ages of children. • Ability to take on ideas for children.	Level 2 or 3, e.g. NVQ level 2 or 3; Take 10 for play
Childminder/ Nanny	Works with children of different ages in a home setting	• Ability to work alone with a baby or child. • Good skills with parents. • Reliable and safety conscious.	Level 3, e.g. Level 3 Diploma in Childcare and Education
Nursery/ Play group assistant	Works in a nursery or play group with children under 5 years	• Ability to work as part of a team. • Good at planning activities. • Good skills with working with parents.	Level 2, e.g. Level 2 Diploma in Childcare and Education; Certificate in Playgroup Practice
Nursery manager or Play group leader	Has responsibility in a nursery or playgroup	• Ability to lead a team. • Good at paperwork. • Good skills with parents. • Good at planning.	Level 3/4, e.g. Level 3 Diploma in Childcare and Education; NVQ 3/4; Diploma in Pre-school Practice
Teaching assistant	Works alongside a teacher with groups or individual children aged 5+	• Ability to follow instructions carefully. • Ability to read and write fairly well. • Ability to manage children's behaviour.	Level 2, although many schools prefer level 3, e.g. NVQ 3; Diploma in Childcare and Education
Teacher	Works in school	• Ability to work with large groups of children. • Ability to manage children's behaviour. • Ability to work with parents and in a team. • Good knowledge of how children learn and develop.	Degree, but you will need a level 3 qualification first

Level of qualifications

The chart on the right shows you what the levels of qualification mean and gives a guide to how long qualifying might take. Your tutor will advise you which level of qualification you are ready to do next.

Types of qualification

There are different types of qualification, although most qualifications can be either full or part time.

College or centre-based courses

You will be expected to attend classes. You will need to do regular homework and assignments. College or centre-based courses have start dates and finish dates, so you will know how long the course should take you.

- Very good if you find it hard to study alone or need someone to help you.
- Part-time courses are good for people who need to keep working.

Distance learning

You will be expected to do a lot of studying by yourself. The speed at which you gain your qualification will depend on how well you work.

- Good for people who are very disciplined and who cannot get to college.
- Good for people who want to work while studying.

Work-based learning through a college or training provider

You need to provide evidence of your skills and knowledge. You need to be very organised and good at following instructions. You have to work by yourself, although some colleges and training providers also provide part-time classes. The speed at which you qualify will depend on how well you work.

- Good for people who want to work while they learn.
- Good for people who do not like doing assignments or tests.
- Good for people who want to work very hard and qualify quickly or who may need to take some time off from their studying.

Level	What this usually means	Length of time (guide)
Level 1	Introductory or foundation level	Depends on course
Level 2	Able to work under supervision	Approx. 12–18 months
Level 3	Able to work alone; may move to a degree course	18 months to 2 years

Activity

In pairs, think about the following questions.

- Which ages of children do you work with best?
- Do you work better in a large or small setting?
- Do you enjoy working by yourself or with others?
- How well do you work with parents?
- Do you find studying interesting?
- What is your attendance at college like?
- Do you find written work difficult?
- Are you interested in staying at college?
- Could you do a full-time or part-time course?
- Would you like to take a qualification while working?
- How easy do you find it to study by yourself?
- How easy would it be to find a job?

Summary

- There are many opportunities for working in childcare.
- Different jobs require different levels of qualifications.
- There are different ways of studying for qualifications.

End of unit summary

To decide what you need to do next you need to consider what you have achieved during the course and what you have enjoyed doing.

End of unit task: Course review

1 Answer the questions in the flow chart and use them to help you decide what you need to do next.

2 Copy out and complete the form below:

During this course I have learned:

....
....
....
....
....

In the next few months I would like to:

....
....
....
....
....

My goal is to become:

....
....
....
....
....

Have you gained in confidence during the course?

In what areas do you feel more confident?

Have you enjoyed working with children in settings?

Which setting did you most enjoy being in?

Would you like to work in a childcare setting?

What age of children would you like to work with?

What training do you need to work with this age of children?

Where can you get this training?

Have your written skills improved?

Do you need any further help with reading or writing?

What support is available to help you with your study skills?

Do you feel confident working as part of a group?

Are you able to communicate with adults in childcare settings?

How well do you feel that you communicate with children?

Which unit of the course have you most enjoyed?

What did you learn from this unit?

What do you feel that you have learned about working with children?

Are there any areas of study that you have not enjoyed?

Have you been able to keep up to date with your coursework?

How easy have you found it to study?

Would you like to do some further training?

Back to the real world

You have now begun to think about what you might do next. You have also learned about how to manage children's behaviour and signs that children might have been abused.

1 Can you explain what you would do if you thought that a child had been abused?

2 Can you describe one way in which you can help children to show positive behaviour?

3 Can you explain what is meant by distance learning?

Glossary

abuse Being treated badly

boundary setting Letting children know what behaviour we expect of them

goals for behaviour Behaviour that we should be encouraging children to show

positive behaviour Behaviour that is desirable

positive reinforcement Rewards for positive behaviour

unwanted behaviour Actions or speech that are unacceptable

My story

Molly

I had always wanted to work with children but had difficulty in reading and writing, and so was told that it would be hard to get a job working in a nursery. Luckily, I did the Caring for Children course at my local college. The tutors were really brilliant and during the year my reading and writing really came on. When I finished the course, I decided to stay on at college and do the level 2. I am now working at the nursery where I did one of my placements and am studying for my NVQ level 3. It has been hard, but next year I will be fully qualified. It's like a dream come true.

Index